S0-AVP-046

DISCARDED

Introduction to Mendelian Genetics and Gene Action

Paul W. Sciulli
The Ohio State University

Burgess Publishing Company
Minneapolis, Minnesota

COLLEGE OF THE SEQUOIAS
LIBRARY.

Copyright © 1978 by Burgess Publishing Company
Printed in the United States of America
Library of Congress Catalog Card Number 77-074168
ISBN: 0-8087-4542-5

All rights reserved. No part of this book may be reproduced in any form
whatsoever, by photograph or mimeograph or by any other means, by
broadcast or transmission, by translation into any kind of language, nor
by recording electronically or otherwise, without permission in writing
from the publisher, except by a reviewer, who may quote brief passages
in critical articles and reviews.

0   9   8   7   6   5   4   3   2   1

THE MODERN PHYSICAL ANTHROPOLOGY SERIES
Under the editorship of
Frank E. Poirier
The Ohio State University

EDITOR'S FOREWORD

When this book and other titles in the Modern Physical Anthropology series are used to complement my text *In Search of Ourselves* or any other introductory anthropology text, you will find that they expand the information presented in most of these texts and often hold viewpoints that vary from the ones offered in the texts. The Modern Physical Anthropology series is designed to allow for the presentation of divergent viewpoints so that students will become aware that much remains to be done and that physical anthropology is an alive and exciting field of endeavor.

PREFACE

The title of this book expresses its intention: to introduce some basic concepts of Mendelian genetics and gene action in humans. This book is written for students who are enrolled in introductory courses and who have little or no background in the biological sciences. To this end I have tried to be brief and have sought relatively uncomplicated examples which, however, still represent the underlying principles of heredity. This book may thus be used with other texts on human genetics or as a supplement to texts on physical anthropology or human biology.

The discussion of heredity begins with a review of the experiments of Gregor Mendel. The discussion of these simple, straightforward experiments will explain the laws governing the transmission of genes from parent to offspring. Chapter 2 will show how these laws operate in humans, and Chapter 3 will consider, in the most basic sense, how genes work. Chapter 3 begins with a review of the experiments leading up to and including the discovery of the genetic material. The history of these advances is included because they changed many ideas that scientists had long taken for granted and stimulated new fields of enquiry that have, in the last quarter century, found solutions to human problems once thought insoluble. Chapter 3 includes a discussion of the chemical nature of genes and their action and students without a chemistry course may find it helpful to consult an elementary text. A glossary is provided which includes many of the new terms introduced in the text.

CONTENTS

chapter one

THE ROOTS OF MODERN GENETICS

In 1866 Gregor Mendel presented a comprehensive report concerning his experiments in plant hybridization. Mendel began his work with the modest hope that the results would help to establish rules, if any existed, which governed the appearance of characteristics (such as height of plant or color of seeds) in various generations of pea plant hybrids. As we shall see, the results of Mendel's experiments not only established the basic rules governing the appearance of characteristics in plants, but these rules also became the foundation for the science of heredity, the laws of which are applicable to all organisms including humans.

Mendel's Experiments in Plant Hybridization

How did Mendel, an Augustinian monk working alone in his monastery garden, arrive at the results leading to the most profound and basic aspect of the biological sciences? The answer to this question is lost to history. However, we can examine Mendel's background and his work and gain some insights into his genius.

Gregor Mendel was born in 1822 in an area of eastern Europe now part of Czechoslovakia. After entering an Augustinian monastery he was ordained a priest in 1847. Shortly thereafter he was enrolled at the University of Vienna, where he acquired training in the natural sciences, especially physics and mathematics. (This training in the natural sciences provided Mendel with many skills, notably mathematical, which would be invaluable in the interpretation of his experimental data.) After graduating, Mendel returned to his monastery at Brünn and in 1854 began teaching and experimenting. In 1856 Mendel initiated the famous series of experiments which led to the definition of the laws of heredity.

Prior to the more famous experiments, however, Mendel studied the transmission of characters from parent to offspring and from generation to generation in a number of organisms. These early experiments no doubt guided Mendel both in his methodology and in his final choice for a suitable organism with which to study heredity. For example, Mendel had investigated character transmission in bees, mice, and various plants, and he knew of similar work being conducted by others. He was also aware that the unifying thread connecting all of these early studies in heredity was that little useful information was obtained.

Mendel noted from his own experiments and those of others various reasons for the lack of understanding heredity. First, the characteristics being studied were not consistently present in every generation. Part of this problem was that the expression or appearance of a physical characteristic would often change from one generation to another. Some of this variability was in the characteristics themselves; however, much of it was an artifact of the observer's "definition" of the characteristic. The size of various structures is an example of **trait**[1] variability (the terms *trait* and *characteristic* will be used interchangeably). How could one consistently distinguish, for example, between a small, medium-sized leaf and a medium, small-sized leaf when the trait (size) is continuous (that is, all sizes are possible)? To overcome ambiguity in trait identification, Mendel knew he needed an organism which exhibited traits that were discontinuous, meaning that there would be no overlap in the expression of characteristics—the appearance of a trait would be of the either/or type.

Mendel noted a second reason for not obtaining useful results in experiments concerning heredity. It was simply that individuals were very often placed in the wrong generation; parents, their offspring, and the progeny of the latter were frequently intermingled. To avoid assigning individuals to the wrong generation, Mendel knew he would have to keep an accurate record of the individuals and the generations to which they belong. An organism, such as a plant, whose offspring are associated with it (seeds) would make the keeping of records much easier.

A third source of confusion, as Mendel saw it, was that many experiments produced large numbers of individuals of various types and the rela-

---

[1] Boldface type indicates a term defined in the glossary.

tionship between the types was not always straightforward. For example, if in a given generation 5,793 plants had, say, red flowers and 2,170 had yellow flowers, a stated relationship of 5,793 plants with red flowers to 2,170 plants with yellow flowers is not as clear as saying there are about 3 plants with red flowers to every 1 plant with yellow flowers. Thus, Mendel, in order to keep the results clear and well organized, would ascertain the least complex statistical relationship between the various discontinuous traits in every generation. As we shall see, these three considerations greatly simplified the performance, analysis, and interpretation of Mendel's experiments. These methodological considerations, above all else, enabled Mendel to uncover regularities in the transmission of characters where others such as Charles Darwin, whose experiments produced results similar to Mendel's, failed. Darwin had the answer, but not the methodology to observe it.[2]

Mendel's plan of simplifying the approach to the study of heredity was time consuming. Eight years (1856-1863) were spent in experimentation. Initially, experiments were performed in order to find a suitable organism. From past experience Mendel knew that the common pea plant (genus *Pisum*) possessed several qualities making it a most favorable experimental subject with which to study heredity. For example, the floral structure of pea plants is peculiar in that its configuration enables easy self-fertilization while also affording protection against natural cross-fertilization. Thus Mendel could either artificially self-fertilize or cross-fertilize plants and be almost sure that the resulting offspring were indeed produced by the chosen parents. Secondly, because offspring (the seeds) were associated with the parents, it would not be difficult to place individuals in their correct generations. Finally, and importantly, pea plants will flourish with minimal care. Thus, one investigator with other duties could produce a large number of plants for study.

The initial two years of Mendel's experiments were spent searching for characteristics with constant, easily recognized expressions in each generation. Mendel found seven characteristics in the pea plant fitting this requirement (see chart, page 4). All seven traits were expressed as either of their two listed alternatives; none was intermediate in expression.

Mendel then produced, by self-fertilization, strains of plants that showed only one of the two expressions for a characteristic. For example, one strain may exhibit only tall plants in all generations while another produces only small plants. These "pure" or parental strains could now be crossed among themselves, with respect to the alternate forms of the traits, to produce hybrid plants. The form of the characteristics in the hybrid would then be noted.

---

[2]Charles Darwin's own experiments in breeding hybrid plants yielded results with essentially a whole-number ratio (3:1) of character expressions. The following pages will show the significance Darwin did not grasp.

Characteristic	Expression	
	Either	*Or*
1. Form of ripe seed	Smooth	Wrinkled
2. Color of endosperm	Yellow	Green
3. Color of seed coat	Grey	White
4. Form of ripe seed pods	Smooth	Constricted
5. Color of unripe seed pods	Green	Yellow
6. Position of flowers	Along stem	Top of stem
7. Length of stem	Tall, 6 to 7 feet	Short, 0.75 to 1.50 feet

Results of Mendel's Experiments

Mendel experimented with all seven of the characteristics independently by crossing two strains differing in the expression of one of the characters. For example, Mendel crossed plants having smooth seeds with plants having wrinkled seeds. The parental generation is usually symbolized as P and its offspring, the first filial generation, as F_1. Thus, the smooth with wrinkled cross can be designated in a shortened manner as:

P: smooth x wrinkled

The actual results of this experiment are quite simple:

P: smooth x wrinkled
F_1: 100% smooth

All of the seeds in the F_1 generation of this experiment were smooth. Furthermore, each of the other six crosses produced an F_1 generation exhibiting only one of the alternate forms of the trait. In the list of characteristics and their expressions above, the forms under the column headed *Either* appeared at a 100% frequency in the F_1 generations.

The experiments were continued by self-fertilizing the F_1 generation. The resulting offspring are in the second filial generation, or the F_2. Again, we can look at the smooth x wrinkled cross, which exemplifies the results obtained from all F_2 generations.

P: smooth x wrinkled
F_1: 100% smooth
F_2: 5,474 seeds smooth
1,850 seeds wrinkled

The most obvious fact that emerges when the F_2 generation is observed is that the alternate form of the characteristic which was "lost" in the F_1 (in this case wrinkled) appears again in the F_2. However, the relationship be-

4

tween smooth and wrinkled in the F_2 is not really obvious. The F_2 results can be simplified somewhat by stating the percentage of smooth and wrinkled instead of the actual numbers. If this is done it can be seen that in the F_2 smooth seeds are present at a frequency of $5,474/7,324 = 0.747$ or approximately 75% and wrinkled at a frequency of $1,850/7,324 = 0.253$ or 25%. This can be stated in another way by saying that smooth seeds are 3 times more frequent than wrinkled seeds, or that the ratio of smooth to wrinkled seeds is $3:1$. The F_2 generation of the other six experiments was also reported to have a $3:1$ ratio between the characteristic present at 100% frequency in the F_1 and the characteristic lost in the F_1.[3]

Thus, for the first two hybrid generations (F_1 and F_2) Mendel noted three consistencies:
1. For all seven traits the F_1 generation possessed only one of the alternate forms. Both were never present.
2. The alternate form of the trait "lost" or hidden in the F_1 reappeared in the F_2 at a 25% frequency.
3. These results were always the same regardless of the sex of the parent exhibiting the alternate forms. A parent with wrinkled seeds providing pollen for a parent with smooth seeds gave the same results as a parent with round seeds providing pollen for a parent with wrinkled seeds.

From these results Mendel noted that traits could be hidden (in the F_1) but not lost. As a result of this he termed the traits that could be hidden "recessive traits" and their alternate forms "dominant traits." Since the recessive traits were not expressed in the F_1, whatever factors that determine recessive traits must have been hidden because the trait is not lost. Therefore, traits hidden in the F_1 are determined by recessive *factors*. It follows then that dominant *factors* (which show **dominance** over recessive factors) determine the traits not hidden in the F_1. Extending this reasoning to the parental generation (pure lines) we can see that parents with dominant traits must possess only dominant factors and parents with recessive traits have only recessive factors because they were bred to show only one of the traits and they did so consistently. The F_1 generation plants, however, must contain both the dominant and the recessive factors because they produce offspring having either dominant or recessive traits.

The results and interpretation of the experiments discussed thus far would have been a significant contribution to the study of, among other fields, evolution. During the 19th century a popular theory used to explain the mechanism of heredity was that of a blending of fluids (for example, in

[3]Mendel's results seem to be "too good," that is, too close to what is expected. R. A. Fisher and Sewall Wright each discuss the possible reasons underlying the excessive goodness of fit (see *Suggestions for Further Reading*).

animals such terms as *blood, bloodlines,* and *good blood* are often used) so that offspring were considered intermediate between, or an average of, the parents. Initially, Charles Darwin employed this theory of blending as the hereditary mechanism underlying species variations and, of course, it was upon the variations that natural selection acted. It was this aspect of Darwin's theory of natural selection that was most controversial and most criticized.[4] The lack of a convincing mechanism to explain the hereditary basis of variation made many biologists cautious about accepting the total theory of natural selection. In fact, Darwin never could adequately explain the mechanism of heredity which was the crux of this theory of natural selection. Much controversy could have been avoided if Mendel's work had been appreciated by his contemporaries.

Mendel's results indicated that blending was not the sole mechanism of heredity, at least in pea plants, if it was a mechanism at all. The results indicated, rather, that the factors controlling the traits were particulate in nature (that is, they behaved as indivisible particles, not as a fluid). But Mendel also wondered how many factors determined a trait. The first two generations of pea plants do not yield enough information to answer this question. However, the next generation produced by Mendel, the F_3, gives the needed information.

The F_3 generation was produced by self-fertilization of the F_2 plants. Mendel noted that the F_2 plants possessing recessive traits produced offspring having *only* recessive traits. These F_2 plants behaved like the "recessive parents" (pure lines) when self-fertilized. F_2 plants with dominant traits, however, did not always produce only plants having dominant traits in the F_3. In the experiment we have been discussing (the one concerned with seed form), the F_2 dominant parents could be divided into two types based on their F_3 offspring: those that produced offspring with only round seeds (dominant) and those that produced both round and wrinkled plants in a 3:1 ratio. The actual results showed that of the 565 F_2 plants with smooth seeds, 193 produced F_3 offspring with only smooth seeds and the remaining 372 plants each produced smooth and wrinkled plants. Thus 372/565 or about 2/3 acted like F_1 plants exhibiting dominant traits. Diagrammatically this breeding experiment produced the results shown on page 7. Further generations, the F_4, F_5, etc., derived from the F_3 showed similar results. The offspring of plants with wrinkled seeds, as always, produced plants with only wrinkled seeds. The F_3 plants derived from F_2 plants producing only smooth seeds always had smooth seeds themselves and always produced F_4 offspring with

---

[4]In 1867, F. Jenkins criticized this theory on the basis that variation would be reduced by one-half in each generation of blending, so variation upon which natural selection could act would soon no longer remain in the population.

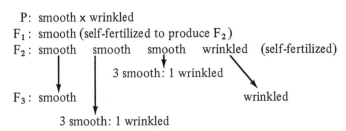

P: smooth x wrinkled

F_1: smooth (self-fertilized to produce F_2)

F_2: smooth   smooth   smooth   wrinkled   (self-fertilized)

3 smooth: 1 wrinkled

F_3: smooth   wrinkled

3 smooth: 1 wrinkled

smooth seeds. Whenever a plant produced offspring in a ratio of 3 smooth: 1 wrinkled, 1/3 of the smooth offspring produced only smooth offspring and 2/3 of the smooth offspring produced both smooth and wrinkled offspring. These results also held true for the remaining six crosses. The F_1 always consisted of 100% dominant plants (plants exhibiting the dominant traits), the F_2 produced 3 dominant to 1 recessive, and the F_3 always conformed to the pattern seen in the seed form experiment.

These results clearly show that plants producing offspring with both dominant and recessive types contain both the dominant and the recessive factor. Although the recessive factor may be hidden, it cannot be lost. We can now return to the question posed earlier. How many factors does each plant contain? We have just seen that some plants must contain at least two factors, a dominant (D) and a recessive (R). These are plants that give rise to offspring in a 3:1 ratio. If we symbolize these plants as DR, then plants producing offspring with only dominant traits must be DD while RR plants then are those producing only offspring with recessive traits. Since plants contain only two factors under this hypothesis,[5] when mating occurs only one factor must be contributed by each parent (in self-fertilization one factor is contributed by the male part of the plant and one by the female). We can assume for the sake of argument that each factor is present in equal numbers and the chance of either being contributed to the offspring is also equal. Thus when a fertilization occurs each parent contributes one randomly chosen factor.

Let's work through the mating presented above and see if the observed results fit the hypothesis. Since in the above mating smooth is the dominant trait and wrinkled the recessive, we can symbolize the factor for smooth as S (large S) and the factor for wrinkled as s (small s). The parental generation is thus SS x ss. According to the present hypothesis, when these plants are crossed each parent should contribute one randomly chosen factor. Since smooth plants only have S factors and wrinkled plants only s, the offspring or the F_1 must be Ss. When this Ss F_1 type is self-fertilized the mating can

---

[5]It's always easiest to start with the simplest hypothesis and make assumptions that will further simplify analysis. If we find this does not work we can move on to more complicated ideas.

be considered of the type *Ss* x *Ss*. Again each parent or each sexual part of the plant will contribute only one randomly chosen factor. *Since each factor is equally frequent and chosen randomly we have to find all the combinations from each parent.* The male (pollen) parent can produce and contribute equally either an *S* or *s* factor. This is also true of a female egg. Thus, the possible combinations are:

		Female (egg)	
		S	*s*
Male	*S*	*SS*	*Ss*
(pollen)	*s*	*Ss*	*ss*

These are the exact types, and in the same ratio, as observed in the F_2. Three-fourths of the plants have the dominant characteristic (*SS, Ss, Ss*) and 1/4 have the recessive characteristic (*ss*)—a 3:1 ratio. Further, of the plants with the dominant characteristic (*SS, Ss, Ss*), 1/3 are of the same type as the pure-line parent (*SS*) and 2/3 are of the F_1 type (*Ss, Ss*). Again, this is what was observed. Thus Mendel showed that *hybrids* (F_1 type) *between two pure parental lines contain both parental factors and when the hybrids mate these factors separate, or segregate, from each other and are randomly passed on to their offspring.* This phenomenon of **segregation** has come to be known as *Mendel's First Law* or the *Law of Segregation*. These results have been demonstrated time and again for many hybrid generations in many species.

It was by studying the alternate forms of single traits that Mendel arrived at the Law of Segregation. After making this discovery he turned his attention to the behavior of alternate forms of *two* characteristics simultaneously. With this end in mind Mendel produced by self-fertilization two pure lines, one with smooth *and* yellow seeds and one with green *and* wrinkled seeds. From the earlier experiments Mendel knew that smooth and yellow were controlled by dominant factors and green and wrinkled by recessive factors. The mating of these two lines produced, as expected because of dominance, F_1 plants with only smooth and yellow seeds. Thus,

P: smooth yellow x green wrinkled
F_1: 100% smooth yellow

The F_1 when self-fertilized, however, produced seeds in a ratio not seen before. The results were:

F_1: smooth yellow (self-fertilized)
F_2 seeds: 315 smooth yellow: 108 smooth green: 101 wrinkled yellow: 32 wrinkled green
F_2 ratio: 9:3:3:1

How can these results be explained and be consistent with the earlier findings? This problem can be approached in two ways. First we can diagram the crosses, taking into account various simplifying assumptions, and second we can look at the expected results in terms of probability. When diagramming the crosses we know two facts from the prior experiments: (1) smooth and yellow are dominant and wrinkled and green are recessive, and (2) the dominant factors are independent of the recessive factors for each trait. But what is the relationship between the traits? First let us represent the cross as:

P: *SSYY* (smooth yellow) x *ssyy* (wrinkled green)

Since the dominant and recessive factors are independent for each trait, let us assume they are independent between the traits.[6] If they are independent between the traits, the pollen and egg must contain all of the combinations of factors for both traits. Thus, the parent's egg or pollen contains the following combinations:

	Y	Y
S	SY	SY
S	SY	SY

and

	y	y
s	sy	sy
s	sy	sy

In all cases the smooth yellow parent produces only one type of *gamete* (a general term referring to reproductive cells, that is, eggs, pollen, sperm), *SY*, and the wrinkled green parent also produces only one type of gamete, *sy*. Thus,

P: *SSYY* x *ssyy*

P gametes: *SY*   *sy*

F_1: *SsYy*

Because of dominance the F_1 seeds should all appear smooth and yellow. That is what was actually seen by Mendel. Independence between the traits can explain the results so far. Let's approach the production of the F_2 in the same way. We saw that, according to the hypothesis of independence between traits, the F_1 consisted of the following factors: *SsYy*. Again, if the traits seed form and seed shape are independent, the gametes of either sex should contain all the possible combinations of the factors. We can find the possible combinations in the gametes by:

[6]On page 7 we assumed that the chance of either factor being contributed to an offspring was equal and stated this was a simplifying assumption. Here we will assume that the factors for different traits are independent, that is, have no effect on one another, again to simplify our approach.

Gametes from *Yy*

		Y	y
Gametes from *Ss*	S	SY	Sy
	s	sY	sy

These four types of gametes will be produced by both sexes of F_1 individuals. To find the kinds of F_2 individuals produced we can make a chart like that used above to find the types of gametes, but the margins will now be occupied by the types of gametes produced because we want to know what factors the F_2 individuals will contain. Thus:

Eggs (female gametes)

		SY	Sy	sY	sy
Pollen (males gametes)	SY	SSYY	SSYy	SsYY	SsYy
	Sy	SSYy	SSyy	SsYy	Ssyy
	sY	SsYY	SsYy	ssYY	ssYy
	sy	SsYy	Ssyy	ssYy	ssyy

If both of the factors are independent in each trait and the factors for the different traits are independent, then the F_2 should consist of these 16 types of individuals. Do Mendel's observations conform to expectation? Remember that Mendel found a 9:3:3:1 ratio in the F_2. When the above table is analyzed as to the number of different types it can be seen that 9 individuals are of the type $S\_Y\_$, that is, 9 contain at least one dominant factor of each trait and thus appear as smooth and yellow. The types $ssY\_$ and S_yy each appear 3 times and, because of dominance, appear wrinkled and yellow or smooth and green, respectively. The final individual is $ssyy$ and appears wrinkled and green. Thus, the hypothesis of independence *between* the traits yields expected results identical to the results observed by Mendel—9 smooth yellow: 3 smooth green: 3 wrinkled yellow: 1 wrinkled green.

If the chance for a seed to be smooth or wrinkled is independent of its chance to be yellow or green, that is, if form has no effect on color, then each trait can be analyzed separately and combined by multiplying the chance of each characteristic occurring independently. Thus, the F_1 of a smooth x wrinkled cross would consist entirely of smooth seeds. The F_2 would consist of 3 smooth: 1 wrinkled. Similarly for yellow and green, the F_1 are all yellow and F_2 are 3 yellow: 1 green. If these two traits are *independent*, their frequencies when they are considered together in the F_2 should equal the *products* of the two independent crosses. Thus:

3 yellow: 1 green
x 3 smooth: 1 wrinkled
_____
9 smooth yellow: 3 smooth green: 3 wrinkled yellow: 1 wrinkled green

Mendel crossed the various F_2 plants in order to test the kinds of factors present. The offspring in all cases conformed in type and frequency to those expected if the factors for the different traits were independent. In all these cases, independence between traits could theoretically produce results consistent with Mendel's observations. *Hybrids containing alternate factors for two traits show the separation, or segregation, of one pair of factors independently of the segregation of the other pair.* This finding has become known as *Mendel's Second Law* or the *Law of Independent Assortment*.

From experiments thus far Mendel has shown independence between factors determining a single trait (segregation) and independence between factors determining different traits (independent assortment). One of the final experiments performed by Mendel considered three trait differences. One pure line, or variety, had smooth and yellow seeds and violet flowers (all dominant, *SSYYVV*) and the second variety had wrinkled, green seeds and white flowers (all recessives, *ssyyvv*). The results of this cross could also be explained by independent assortment of the three sets of factors. The F_1 consisted of all smooth yellow seeds and violet flowers (*SsYyVv*) as expected. The number and types of gametes produced by F_1 individuals can be found as before. To check the results as to the number of gametes, let n equal the number of factor pairs that differ in the F_1. The quantity 2^n will give the number of different gametes produced by F_1 individuals. In this case n = 3 and $2^3 = 8$. Thus, the male and female in F_1 will each produce eight types of gametes and, if all the combinations are independent, 64 types of F_2 individuals are expected. If this $F_1 \times F_1$ (or F_1 self-fertilization) is diagrammed, it will be seen that, because of dominance, the 64 types of individuals can be reduced to a ratio of 27:9:9:9:3:3:3:1. Results closely approximating this ratio were observed by Mendel.[7]

_____**Response to Mendel's Work**

The results of Gregor Mendel's eight years of experimentation led him to the discovery of two basic laws of heredity: independence between factors con-

_____

[7] A total of 639 plants were classified as 269 *S_ Y_ V_:* 98 *S_ Y_vv:* 86 *S_yyV_:* 88 *ssY_ V_:* 27 *S_yyvv:* 34 *ssYYvv:* 30 *ssyyV_ :* 7 *ssyyvv*. The expected numbers, based on the expected ratio, are, respectively, 269.6:89.8:89.8:89.8:30.0:30.0:30.0:10.0. See footnote 3 in this chapter.

trolling a trait and independence between sets of factors controlling separate traits. Mendel presented his work to the Brünn Society of Natural Science in 1865 and in the following year his results were published in the Society's Proceedings. Although this journal was widely distributed throughout Europe and even reached America, a response to Mendel's work was lacking. Why? One of the probable reasons was that no one else understood Mendel's "numerology" as it applied to problems in biology. In addition, since most of the knowledge of the cell and reproduction was yet to be established in Mendel's day, his findings must have seemed very abstract, almost arbitrary. Mendel's results also indicated that variability among the hybrid generations could be traced back to the parents—that is, variability was not the product of new factors but rather the new arrangement of factors. Many biologists of Mendel's time were searching for a source of variation in evolution and Mendel's results also indicated that variability among the hybrid generations determined traits. This concept of constancy must have been unacceptable to a 19th-century evolutionist. Many forces were operating at this time which helped obscure Mendel's work.

During the latter half of the 19th century a number of advances were made in the study of cell division. Chromosomes had been discovered and the particular nature of their behavior during cell division was noted. Mathematical approaches to problems in biology were also now more frequent thanks to the impetus of men such as Francis Galton, the 19th-century scholar responsible for introducing the mathematical tool known as regression analysis. Considering these developments, it is not too surprising that in the year 1900 the laws of heredity were rediscovered. It is surprising, however, that the laws were independently rediscovered by three different investigators. Thus, even though Mendel did discover the basic laws of heredity, the development of the science of genetics would have been the same had he never lived. The three rediscoverers of both the laws of heredity and Mendel's work were Hugo De Vries, Carl Correns, and Erick von Tschermak, who published their reports, respectively, in March, April, and June of 1900.[8]

By 1900 much information had been collected concerning cell division and especially the behavior of the dark-staining bodies in the nucleus called **chromosomes.** In 1903 a correspondence between the behavior of chromosomes during cell division and the theoretical behavior of Mendelian factors was pointed out by Walter Sutton and Theodor Boveri. For example, chromosomes were known to be present in pairs, one of maternal origin and one of paternal origin. According to Mendel, factors also occurred in pairs, one of

[8]Von Tschermak's paper was actually not a rediscovery of Mendel's laws since, unlike those of Correns and De Vries, it presented results without the fundamental analysis.

maternal and one of paternal origin. In addition, during the cell division that produced gametes (**meiosis**) the chromosomes of each pair separated, one going to each gamete. This is consistent with Mendel's Law of Segregation. Also during meiosis, chromosome pairs are arranged independently of each other, that is, one pair's arrangement in no way influenced the arrangement of any other pair. This accords with Mendel's Law of Independent Assortment. Finally, gametes contain only *one* chromosome of every pair but each chromosome is united with its partner at fertilization. Mendel's factors are also present singly in gametes and pairs are produced at fertilization. This correspondence is very striking and the hypothesis of Sutton and Boveri that the chromosomes were the vehicles carrying the Mendelian factors was favorably received. Experiments during the following ten years provided a great deal of evidence that the Sutton-Boveri hypothesis was, in fact, true.

The early 1900s also saw a flurry of research aimed at testing Mendel's laws in organisms other than the garden pea. Experiments conducted during this time provided evidence that Mendel's laws were generally applicable to all organisms. However, some results indicated that Mendelian factors were *not always* transmitted independently of each other nor were the expressions of the factors always independent. Later, mainly through the work of Thomas Morgan, the former exception to Mendel's laws was explained. Organisms possess more traits than chromosomes. Since chromosomes are the vehicles carrying the factors controlling traits, more than one factor must be carried by each chromsome. If so, two or more characters will be transmitted together, that is, they will appear **linked** in their transmission from parent to offspring. The second apparent exception to Mendel's laws, the fact that the expression of factors was not always independent, was ultimately explained through investigations into the mode of action of Mendel's factors, initiated by Sewall Wright in 1915. Investigations of this type employed biochemical, physiological, and histological data to determine how Mendelian factors influenced the growth and development of traits. In time it was seen that observable traits are the result of a number of biochemical reactions, each mutually interdependent and each governed by a Mendelian factor. Thus, although two or more Mendelian factors may be transmitted independently, their expressions may be dependent on one another because they govern biochemical reactions in a pathway leading to the same trait. This topic will be explored more fully in Chapter 3.

Included among the various organisms investigated in the early 1900s were humans. The study of our own species presented a number of difficulties, as we shall see in Chapter 2. Nevertheless, in 1909 Sir Archibald Garrod, in his monograph *Inborn Errors of Metabolism,* presented evidence showing that four traits (diseases) in humans were transmitted in Mendelian fashion.

These diseases are: *alkaptonuria, cystinuria, albinism,* and *pentosuria.*[9] Further, Garrod hypothesized that these diseases were the result of blocks in metabolic pathways. His hypothesis was later substantiated and we shall discuss some of these findings in Chapter 3.

As we have seen, during the early 1900s Mendel's laws became well established. Many traits in various organisms were found to produce the ratios observed by Mendel. Included in this group of organisms were humans. In the following two chapters we will explore various human characteristics that show Mendelian types of inheritance. More significantly we will also see how factors produce their effects, that is, how they produce characteristics. This aspect of heredity is important because, as we have seen, some characteristics are the result of a series of reactions, all mutally interdependent. To *fully* understand a trait, the method of its production, its interactions, and its possible interactions with other traits should be known.

[9]Garrod began his studies of inborn errors of metabolism in 1899 with alkaptonuria and by 1902 found this "error" to be fully explainable as governed by a Mendelian recessive factor. See Figure 3.17.

chapter two

MENDEL'S LAWS AND HUMAN HEREDITY

When establishing and testing the laws of heredity, Mendel and others employed organisms whose matings could be easily manipulated and which produced fairly large numbers of offspring per mating. Unfortunately for genetic analysis, humans are not such organisms.

Studying Human Heredity

In order to test the possibility that a characteristic in humans is controlled by *Mendelian factors,* the investigator must search through populations for appropriate matings and then *pool the results of all of the same types of matings to obtain large numbers of offspring.*[1] To ascertain which are the appropriate matings the pedigree (a listing of an individual's biological relatives; for example, Figure 2.3) of the individuals must be obtained so that the kinds of factors in the individuals can be determined. For example, if

---

[1] In genetic analysis a large number of individuals per mating is desirable because, as we have seen, the pair of factors for a trait and the pairs of factors for different traits are independent and transmitted from parent to offspring at random. Thus, purely at random, an individual may transmit only one factor or one combination of two independent factors. This is analogous to flipping a fair coin. If you only flip it once it is quite likely that a head will appear. However, if you flip it 10,000 times it is quite unlikely that heads will appear all 10,000 times. In the latter case you would expect approximately equal numbers of heads and tails. The same logic can be applied to individuals with the factor *Ss.*

an individual possesses a trait that is thought to be controlled by a dominant factor, the individual may be of two types, *AA* or *Aa*. If it is known, however, that only one of the parents of this individual possesses this charac-teristic, it can then be assumed that the individual is of the *Aa* type since one of the parents was *aa* and the other *AA* or *Aa*.

The remainder of this chapter will deal with human characteristics for which it has already been established in the ways outlined above whether genetic control is by dominant, recessive, or other kinds of factors. Our investigation will center on the usual ways in which these factors are transmitted in families and can be recognized. Before the various traits are studied, a new and more useful set of terms will be introduced.

The first new term that will be introduced is **locus** (pl. loci), a segment of a chromosome where the Mendelian factor is located. Each factor occupies a separate locus on the chromosomes of an individual. As we have seen in the last section, chromosomes are present in pairs in most complexly organized species, including humans. The corresponding segments in each pair are, however, collectively referred to as the same locus. Thus the two chromosomes in a pair (**homologous chromosomes**) each contain the same locus and it is located at the same place on each. In fact, the chromosomes in a pair have the same loci along their entire length (see Figure 2.1). The locus, al-

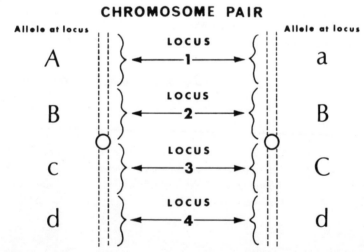

Figure 2.1. Diagram of a pair of chromosomes illustrating the concept of locus and allele. In this simplified example only *one* pair of chromosomes is considered. This pair has four loci, 1 through 4, with alleles Aa at locus 1, BB at locus 2, Cc at locus 3, and dd at locus 4. This "individual" is heterozygous at loci 1 and 3 and homozygous at loci 2 and 4.

though at the same place on each of the chromosomes in a pair, may contain different factors. For example, an individual may be of the type *Aa,* where *A* controls the dominant form of a trait and *a* the recessive form. Each of these factors is present at the locus (which may be thought of as controlling the trait), the dominant factor on one chromosome of the pair and the recessive factor on the other.

Alternate forms of factors are termed **alleles**. In the above example, one locus and two alleles, *A* and *a*, were considered. Various combinations of alleles may also be distinguished. Individuals with the same allele at one locus (*aa* or *AA*) are called **homozygous** for that locus. There are obviously two types of homozygous individuals; homozygous dominant (*AA*) and homozygous recessive (*aa*). Individuals possessing two different alleles at a locus (*Aa*) are termed *heterozygotes,* that is, they are **heterozygous** at this locus (see Figure 2.1).

In the early 1900s various terms were applied to the concept of a Mendelian factor; eventually the term *gene* was adopted. The terms *factor* and *gene* both refer to the object carried by the chromosome which controls the form of a trait. The term *gene* will be employed here since its usage is so widespread. The final terms to be introduced here will enable us to distinguish between the outward appearance of an individual and the type of genes being carried. If the types of alleles present in an individual are known, then the **genotype** is known. The genotype states explicitly the alleles present. If there is dominance in the relationship between the alleles, heterozygotes (*Aa*) appear the same as dominant homozygotes (*AA*). The physical manifestation of the genotype is called the **phenotype**. Thus, *AA* and *Aa* individuals have the same phenotype but different genotypes; *AA* and *Aa* appear the same and show the phenotype of the dominant gene *A*. Using this terminology, we will now look at the hereditary patterns of various human traits.

Dominant Genes

The first types of human traits we will investigate are those controlled by dominant genes. It is not the purpose here to demonstrate that these characters are controlled by dominant genes; this has already been done by the study of many families. Rather, we shall investigate the usual means of transmission of genes in families and the methods and inferences used to support the mode of transmission.

As an example of a character controlled by a dominant gene we shall first look at finger length in humans. Very short fingers, *brachydactyly Al,* is controlled by a dominant gene. The genealogy, or pedigree, of a family exhibiting brachydactyly Al is presented in Figure 2.2. The Roman numerals to

17

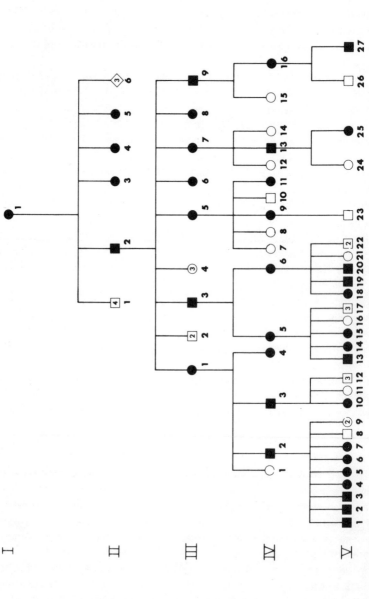

Figure 2.2. Pedigree of a family with brachydactyly A1, a simple dominant trait. Adapted from Farabee, W. C. Inheritance of digital malformations in man. *Papers of the Peabody Museum, Harvard University 3.* Copyright © 1905.

the left of the pedigree indicate the generation. The darkened figures in the pedigree are affected individuals (individuals with brachydactyly), and the open figures indicate unaffected individuals. Males are represented by squares and females by circles. The triangular symbol indicates that the sex of the individual is unknown. Numbers inside symbols tell how many others of that sex are unaffected, and the numbers below the symbols are reference numbers that will enable us to quickly identify any individual in any generation. Horizontal lines connecting males and females indicate a mating. These symbols will be used in all subsequent pedigrees.

Examination of Figure 2.2. reveals some obvious characteristics in the mode of inheritance of dominant traits in general. First, both males and females can transmit the gene for brachydactyly. Second, brachydactyly occurs in every generation; it does not skip generations. The offspring of unaffected individuals are not included in this pedigree since none are affected, illustrating another characteristic of the inheritance of brachydactyly; only affected individuals have affected offspring. Further examination of the pedigree shows that the number of affected individuals (37) from matings in which one or both of the parents are affected is very close to the number of unaffected individuals (36) from such matings. If one excludes from consideration the original case that attracted attention to the family, this is a 1:1 ratio. Although this particular family's pedigree doesn't show it, brachydactyly is generally found with equal frequency in both sexes.[2] How can we explain this pattern? Let's first look at the occurrence of brachydactyly in populations. In all populations brachydactyly is rare. Thus, we can assume that the great majority of individuals who have brachydactyly must be heterozygous since it is unlikely that two individuals each with two rare genes will mate and produce a dominant homozygote. If in fact the great majority of individuals with brachydactyly are heterozygous, say *Bb,* and mate with unaffected individuals, say *bb,* then the ratio of affected to unaffected offspring will be 1:1 since the mating is *Bb* x *bb* (see Figure 2.3).

The mates of individuals having brachydactyly are not presented in the pedigree of brachydactyly. However, all of the mates are unaffected, so the matings do seem to conform to the *Bb* x *bb* type. Because the presence of only one dominant gene will produce brachydactyly, affected offspring must have one affected parent. For the same reason brachydactyly will not skip a generation. If individuals in a generation do not have this trait, even though their parents did, then they *don't* have the gene that causes it. If they don't have the gene for brachydactyly, they then cannot transmit this gene and brachydactyly *won't* appear in their offspring, or, for that matter, in any of their direct descendents unless they mate with individuals who possess

---

[2]See footnote 1 in this chapter.

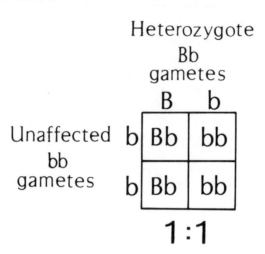

Figure 2.3. Possible offspring of a mating between an individual heterozygous for brachydactyly and an unaffected individual.

this gene (of course this assumes there is no change in the genes controlling this trait, that is, no **mutation**). Thus, brachydactyly *won't* skip a generation and reappear later. Since both males and females can transmit this gene, and since they both are affected with equal frequency, it *doesn't* appear that this trait is linked to any genes determining sex.

We can now look at a second rare dominant trait and perform a similar analysis in order to be fairly certain about the pattern of inheritance for rare dominants. The second trait we shall investigate is white forelock. In this characteristic a band or patch of hair on the front of the head is white. This condition is analogous to white spotting in animals. Figure 2.4 is a pedigree showing the inheritance of white forelocks.

Again we see the same pattern of inheritance. There is essentially a 1:1 ratio between affected (dark symbols) and unaffected (light symbols) individuals, the trait doesn't skip generations, only affected parents produce affected offspring, and both males and females transmit the trait. These characteristics of inheritance are seen for all rare dominant genes. If the gene is more common in a population, there is a greater chance of two heterozygous individuals mating. If a mating of this type (*Bb* x *Bb*) occurs, then the familiar 3:1 ratio of affected to unaffected is expected. One can similarly determine the expected type of offspring from any mating if the parental genotypes are known. One must learn this last bit of information either from the individual's parents and/or the offspring produced by that individual.

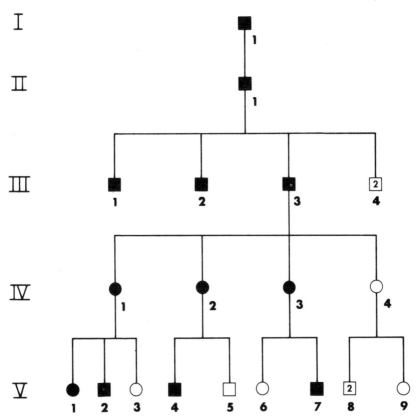

Figure 2.4. Pedigree of a family with white forelock, a simple dominant trait. Adapted from Fitch, L. Inheritance of a white forelock. *Journal of Heredity* 28. p. 414. Copyright © 1937.

In some cases, the genotype of an individual cannot be determined if, for example, the parents *cannot* be observed or if there are few, if any, offspring. Figure 2.5 presents two pedigrees of a dominant character which exemplify this problem. In the first pedigree (A), if only the affected male in generation II (individual II-1) and his mother (I-2) were known, we couldn't be sure if individual II-1 were heterozygous or homozygous dominant. However, his first child (III-1) tells us that he is heterozygous since III-1 is homozygous recessive and therefore must have received a recessive allele from both parents. In the second pedigree (B), II-1 may again be either homozygous or heterozygous, since both of her parents (I-1 and I-2), although exhibiting the trait, may be heterozygotes. Her first two children *don't* give us any useful information since she may have transmitted the dominant gene twice even though she is heterozygous. The third child (III-3) tells us that II-1 must be

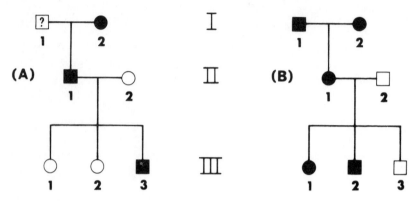

Figure 2.5. Pedigrees of hypothetical simple dominant trait.

heterozygous since this child is homozygous and must have received a recessive allele from her mother. If, however, all children of II-1 were affected we could never be sure of her genotype.

Before discussing other modes of inheritance and their patterns, one final aspect of dominant inheritance should be discussed. This topic originated early in the 1900s soon after the rediscovery of Mendel's laws. Brachydactyly was the first human character to be shown to be controlled by a dominant gene and the speculation arose that since this character was controlled by a dominant gene, enough individuals would eventually possess this gene so that most matings would be between heterozygotes and a 3:1 ratio of individuals with brachydactyly to long-fingered individuals should be observed in populations. However, brachydactyly is very rare in populations, nowhere near 75%. How can this apparent paradox be explained? Thomas Hardy and Wilhelm Weinberg independently explained this paradox in 1908 by showing that the frequency of genes in populations is stable over time if the populations meet certain requirements. This principle has come to be known as the Hardy-Weinberg Equilibrium Law.[3] Thus in most populations brachydactyly will remain a rare gene (will remain at a low frequency) over time. Readers should refer to another book in this series, *Population Genetics,* by Russell Reid, for further explanations of this principle. We are mainly concerned here with the observation that Mendel's laws do hold for dominant genes in human populations.

---

[3] In 1903 William E. Castle also demonstrated theoretical population equilibrium.

The second type of human characteristic that we shall investigate is that controlled by recessive genes. Again, we shall examine pedigrees of two characteristics; albinism, the lack of pigmentation, and phenylketonuria, or PKU, the abnormal buildup of the amino acid phenylalanine and its derivatives. Figure 2.6 is a pedigree of a family exhibiting recessive albinism.[4]

Before examining the pedigree of albinism we should note that since this trait is controlled by recessive alleles, individuals who exhibit the character must possess *both* recessive alleles, that is, they must be homozygous recessive. This, in turn, tells us that each parent of an affected individual must possess *at least* one of the recessive alleles. Thus, the matings that can produce a homozygous recessive individual are *Rr* x *Rr, rr* x *Rr,* or *rr* x *rr.*

A cursory look at the pedigree in Figure 2.6 shows, first, that albinism (dark figures) is present in every other generation; it skips generations. A closer look shows that individuals of both sexes can transmit the alleles controlling albinism. Individuals need not exhibit the character in order to transmit the gene that controls it; *genes, not traits, are transmitted from generation to generation.* It is also evident from the pedigree that affected individuals have unaffected parents. We can explain this pattern by approaching the problem in the manner used for dominant inheritance. If, as in the case with albinism, the recessive allele is rare (in populations), the great majority of individuals *possessing this allele* will be heterozygous. However, most of the *total number of individuals* in the population won't have the allele at all; they will be homozygous dominant. Because very few homozygous recessive individuals are present, the most frequent mating involving individuals with the recessive allele will be *Rr* x *Rr.* Thus, this recessive allele may be "hidden" for generations in families and the trait it controls may seem to appear spontaneously at various times. These times are, of course, when heterozygotes mate. If a recessive allele is very rare in a population, the most likely way to produce a homozygous recessive individual is by mating with an individual from one's own family. Traits controlled by rare recessive genes often are manifested in families in this manner.

Examining the family on the right side of the pedigree, that is, descendents of I-1, we can see that I-1 must be homozygous recessive since she is an albino. Furthermore, her mate, who is not included, was either homozygous dominant or heterozygous since their offspring (II-3) is unaffected. The mate of II-3 must have been heterozygous since some offspring of the mating are albino (homozygous recessive). The unaffected offspring of II-3 could be

---

[4] As with brachydactyly, albinism occurs in a number of forms. We shall consider here only a simple recessive form, albinism I.

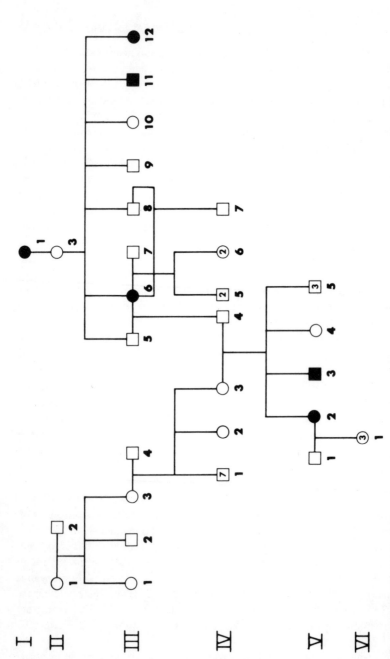

Figure 2.6. Pedigree of a family with albinism I, a simple recessive trait. Adapted from Pipkin, A. C., and Pipkin, S. B. Albinism in Negroes. *Journal of Heredity* 28. p. 425. Copyright © 1942.

24

heterozygous or homozygous dominant. However, given this information we cannot be sure of the alternatives. Similarly, we could assess the genotypes of the remaining individuals descended from I-1. In doing this we see that the reason the character skips generations is that individuals marrying into this family are either homozygous dominant or heterozygous, as would be expected if the recessive allele is rare in the population. This also explains why parents of albinos are usually not albinos themselves.

The left side of the pedigree (the descendents of II-1 and II-2), if considered alone, shows albinism seemingly appearing spontaneously in generation V. This may be because members of this family are heterozygous and have mated with either heterozygous or homozygous dominant individuals; in the first case the production of an albino occurs only 25% of the time and in the latter an albino can't be produced. It must also be considered that III-4, who married into this family, may have been heterozygous and introduced the recessive allele. In either case, albinism has remained "hidden" in this family until the mating between heterozygotes. It was noted on page 23 that traits controlled by rare recessive genes often arise when individuals of the same family mate and produce offspring. The pedigree in Figure 2.6 shows that III-6 and III-8, sister and brother, have produced an offspring who is unaffected. This can be explained by the fact that III-8 is homozygous dominant and therefore his offspring could not express a trait controlled by recessive alleles, or that he is heterozygous but purely by chance (random segregation) he did not transmit the recessive allele to his offspring. Individuals of a family in which a rare recessive allele is segregating have a much higher *chance* of producing an affected offspring, *but only if they carry the alleles in question.*

When many pedigrees of this type are considered it is found that both sexes exhibit albinism in equal frequencies, and that both sexes can transmit the recessive allele controlling this character. Thus, as with the dominant traits we have discussed, albinism is not **sex-linked**.

The second trait we shall consider which is controlled by recessive alleles is phenylketonuria (abbreviated as PKU). Figure 2.7 shows a pedigree of a family with this trait.

On assessing the genotypes of individuals in this family, the same assumptions concerning the rareness of the recessive allele will be employed, since PKU is rare in populations. By examining the pedigree it can be immediately seen that affected individuals (homozygous recessives) result from a mating between first cousins, II-3 and II-4. As previously stated, traits controlled by rare recessives *often* appear as the result of mating with a member of one's own family (consanguineous mating). Again, in this pedigree the recessive allele is hidden by its dominant allele and the trait only appears when hetero-

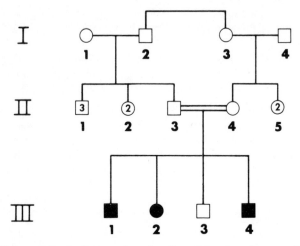

Figure 2.7. Pedigree of a family with phenylketonuria (PKU), a simple recessive trait. Adapted from Kobawaski, T., et al. Oligophrenia pyruvica: three cases in one family. *Shonika Rinsho* 5. p. 6. Copyright © 1952.

zygotes mate. Consideration of *many* pedigrees of PKU show that this rare trait is controlled by recessive alleles. The following regularities of inheritance are the general rules for all traits controlled by rare recessive alleles, including PKU. Such a trait (1) is present in 25% of the offspring of matings between heterozygotes, (2) generally skips one or many generations or appears alternately in many successive generations, (3) is generally exhibited by individuals with unaffected parents, (4) often appears as the result of consanguineous matings, (5) is present in equal frequencies in both sexes, and (6) can be transmitted by both sexes. Additional characteristics of mating involving individuals with rare recessives are: (7) matings between homozygous recessive individuals result in the production of *only* homozygous recessive offspring and (8) matings between homozygous recessive individuals and homozygous dominant individuals result in all offspring with the dominant phenotype (heterozygotes) and matings between homozygous recessive individuals and heterozygotes result in offspring in the ratio 1 homozygous recessive: 1 heterozygote. These eight regularities of inheritance are the general rules for all characters controlled by rare recessive alleles. Comparison between the patterns of inheritance for dominant and recessive genes shows the relative ease in distinguishing them *if many pedigrees and a large number of offspring* can be studied.

	Dominant		*Recessive*

1. Traits controlled by dominant alleles do not skip generations; once lost, as a result of chance segregation, they must be re-introduced.	1. Traits often skip generations or remain hidden for generations; they often only appear or re-appear due to consanguineous mating.
2. Mating between individuals with the trait produces either all offspring with the trait or 75% with the trait and 25% without it.	2. Mating between individuals with the trait produces only individuals with the trait.
3. Mating between affected and unaffected individuals produces either *all affected* or 50% affected and 50% unaffected offspring.	3. Mating between affected and unaffected individuals produces either *all unaffected* or 50% affected and 50% unaffected offspring.

Codominant Genes

In addition to traits controlled by simple dominant or recessive genes, another type of trait is seen which is controlled by codominant alleles. Traits controlled by codominant alleles show **codominance**, meaning that they can simultaneously exhibit properties of both alleles. For example, Mendel investigated the inheritance of flower color in four-o'clocks (genus *Mirabilis*) and found that when he crossed plants that were what we now call homozygous for red flowers with plants homozygous for white flowers, 100% of the F_1 plants exhibited 100% pink flowers. Among members of the F_2, 25% had red flowers, 50% had pink flowers, and 25% had white flowers. These are essentially the same results observed when traits are controlled by simple dominant-recessive alleles, but when alleles are codominant, the influence of each can be seen in the heterozygote (pink).

Many traits, in a variety of species including humans, are controlled by codominant alleles. We shall investigate the inheritance of two human traits controlled by codominant alleles: the Hopkins-2 hemoglobin variant and sickle cell trait. The allele controlling the Hopkins-2 hemoglobin variant governs the structure of the alpha (α) chain of hemoglobin. The allele for sickle cell trait governs the structure of the beta (β) chain of hemoglobin. Hemoglobin is the major oxygen-carrying molecule in humans. The pedigree in Figure 2.8 shows the inheritance of the Hopkins-2 hemoglobin variant.

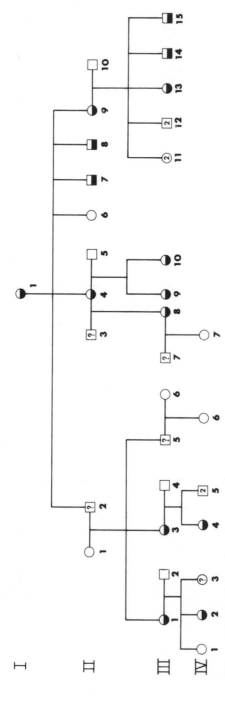

Figure 2.8. Pedigree of a family with the α-chain variant, Hopkins-2, a codominant trait. Adapted from Bradley, T. B. Hopkins-2 hemoglobin: a revised pedigree with data on blood a serum groups. *Bulletin of Johns Hopkins Hospital* 108. pp. 75-79. Copyright © 1961.

Because the alleles for normal hemoglobin (Hb A) and Hopkins-2 are co-dominant, three types of individuals can be distinguished at this locus[5] : individuals with normal hemoglobin, $\alpha^A \alpha^A$ (homozygous), individuals with both normal hemoglobin and Hopkins-2, $\alpha^A \alpha^{Ho-2}$ (heterozygous), and individuals with Hopkins-2 hemoglobin, $\alpha^{Ho-2} \alpha^{Ho-2}$. The main difference between the inheritance of codominant versus either recessive or dominant alleles is that heterozygotes can be determined in the former case. In the pedigree of Figure 2.8, all individuals exhibiting the Hopkins-2 variant are heterozygotes (symbols half-shaded) and thus of the genotype $\alpha^A \alpha^{Ho-2}$. When the variant co-dominant allele is rare, the pattern observed in dominant inheritance can be employed to analyze pedigrees, noting of course that heterozygotes can be distinguished and that the mating of two heterozygotes will in the long run produce $\alpha^A \alpha^A$, $\alpha^A \alpha^{Ho-2}$, and $\alpha^{Ho-2} \alpha^{Ho-2}$ individuals in a 1:2:1 ratio. Matings between homozygotes for the "normal" allele (α^A) and heterozygotes should produce a 1:1 ratio of homozygous "normals" to heterozygotes. This type of mating is exemplified by II-9 with II-10. II-9 is heterozygous ($\alpha^A \alpha^{Ho-2}$), II-10 is homozygous normal ($\alpha^A \alpha^A$), and the offspring (III-11 to III-15) are in the ratio 4 "normal" to 3 heterozygous, close to the expected 1:1 ratio.

A second characteristic controlled by a codominant allele is sickle cell trait. The pedigree in Figure 2.9 shows a family which is segregating for this allele. Figures with the upper half lined are heterozygous for sickle cell ($\beta^A \beta^S$) and are referred to as individuals with sickle cell trait. Only individuals with sickle cell trait and homozygotes for normal hemoglobin (β^A) are present in this pedigree.

In Figure 2.9 where the genotypes of both parents are known it is seen that all matings are of the type $\beta^A \beta^A \times \beta^A \beta^S$ and the expected ratio of offspring is 1 $\beta^A \beta^A$: 1 $\beta^A \beta^S$. The observed ratio is 5 $\beta^A \beta^A$: 3 $\beta^A \beta^S$, close to the 1:1 expected ratio. Since sickle cell trait is controlled by a codominant allele and is relatively rare, the pedigree can be considered with the same assumptions used when investigating the Hopkins-2 variant.

Because heterozygotes are distinguishable when considering codominant alleles (each allele contributes to the phenotype), the analysis of pedigrees requires fewer assumptions concerning the genotypes of individuals. For heterozygotes with codominant alleles *the phenotype is the same as the genotype.*

The pedigrees presented here for the Hopkins-2 hemoglobin variant and for sickle cell trait are in reality the same. Both of these traits are segregating in the family. This gives us a chance to observe Mendel's Second Law, the

---

[5]The alpha locus is represented by α and the alleles by the superscript. For beta chain variants, β represents the locus.

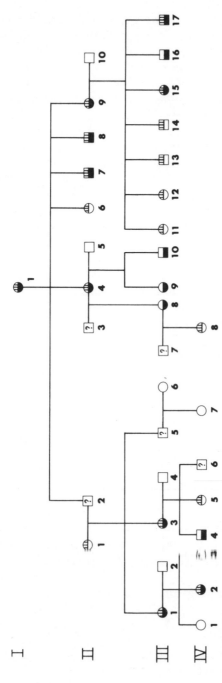

Figure 2.9. Pedigree of a family with sickle cell trait, a β-chain hemoglobin variant inherited as a codominant. The upper halves of the figures refer to sickle cell trait, the lower halves to the Hopkins-2 variant. See text for explanation. Adapted from Bradley, T. B. Hopkins-2 hemoglobin: a revised pedigree with data on blood a serum groups. *Bulletin of Johns Hopkins Hospital* 108. pp. 75-79. Copyright © 1961.

Law of Independent Assortment. It has been established from various lines of evidence, including pedigrees of this kind, that the Hopkins-2 variant and sickle cell trait are controlled by alleles at independent loci. Thus we should be able to observe certain characteristics in this pedigree that are indicative of the operation of Mendel's Second Law.

We shall now return to the pedigree of the sickle cell trait (Figure 2.9). The top parts of the figures, where lined, indicate individuals with sickle cell trait and the lower halves, where shaded, indicate heterozygotes for the Hopkins-2 variant. Since the alleles controlling the variant forms are at independent loci and all matings where the genotypes of both parents are known are of the type $\alpha^A \alpha^{Ho-2} \beta^A \beta^S \times \alpha^A \alpha^A \beta^A \beta^A$, we should expect four types of possible offspring: individuals with normal hemoglobin ($\alpha^A \alpha^A \beta^A \beta^A$), individuals with sickle cell trait ($\alpha^A \alpha^A \beta^A \beta^S$), Hopkins-2 heterozygotes ($\alpha^A \alpha^{Ho-2} \beta^A \beta^A$), and individuals who are heterozygous for Hopkins-2 and have sickle cell trait ($\alpha^A \alpha^{Ho-2} \beta^A \beta^S$). With a large number of matings these four types should be at equal frequencies. Examining the matings with known genotypes in Figure 2.8 (II-4 with II-5, II-9 with II-10, III-1 with III-2, and III-3 with III-4), we can see that *all four types of offspring are present.* However, due to chance, the frequencies of the four types are not equal in this pedigree.

When many pedigrees are studied and pooled, human characters controlled by alleles at independent loci do exhibit the ratios expected according to Mendel's Law of Independent Assortment. If sickle cell trait and Hopkins-2 weren't known to be controlled by independent loci, the pedigree studied here wouldn't prove independent assortment of the loci involved since the family sizes are rather small. Many pedigrees and a variety of other kinds of data, which we shall discuss in the last section, are usually required to show independence of two loci. However, the pedigree in Figure 2.9 suggests independent assortment.

Multiple Alleles

Thus far we have considered only two alleles at a locus. Although any one individual can possess only two alleles (because chromosomes are in pairs), there may be more than two alleles in the population to which the individual belongs. A good example of this condition, termed *multiple allelism,* is the ABO blood group. Because there are more than two alleles, there are more than three genotypes possible. Considering the three principle alleles[6] of the ABO blood group I^A, I^B, and I^O, we find there are six genotypes: $I^A I^A$, $I^B I^B$, $I^O I^O$, $I^A I^O$, $I^B I^O$, and $I^A I^B$. The relationship $n(n+1)/2$ can be used to

---

[6] In this notation I represents the locus and the superscripts the alleles.

determine the number of genotypes possible, where n is the number of alleles in the population.

When considering multiple allelism we must be prepared to deal with various combinations of allelic interactions, that is, dominance, recessivity, and codominance. It has been determined that in the ABO blood group the I^A and I^B alleles are codominant, and that both are dominant to the I^O allele. Thus, phenotypically four types of individuals can be distinguished: type A, type B, type O, and type AB. There are actually more alleles present in the ABO blood group than indicated here. However, for our purposes it is not incorrect to consider only three alleles with the allelic interactions stated. Further discussion of the ABO blood groups can be found in the book *Blood Groups* by Laurence H. Snyder. The pedigree in Figure 2.10 shows the segregation of the ABO alleles in a family.

As opposed to the other traits studied thus far, the alleles for A, B, and O are all relatively frequent in most populations. Thus, there is a good chance that there are individuals homozygous for I^A, I^B, and I^O. Since the I^O allele is recessive to the others, individuals with type O blood must be homozygous. This is seen in individuals II-12 and II-13. They must both be of the genotype $I^O I^O$. I-3 and his descendants may exhibit homozygosity for the I^A allele. However, since we are dealing with a small number of offspring, chance segregation may have caused the I^O allele to be present only with an I^A allele in these individuals. The genotypes for other individuals in this pedigree may be determined in a similar manner. The ABO blood group alleles show no relationship to the sex of an individual.

Simple Sex-Linked Inheritance _____

In the previous examples of simple dominant, recessive, and codominant inheritance, we have noted that the traits and their patterns of inheritance were in no way related to the sex of individuals. However, as we shall see presently, there are a number of traits that do exhibit a definite pattern of inheritance by being associated with the sex of individuals. Before discussing these traits and their patterns of inheritance, a brief outline of the general determiners of biological sex will be helpful.

Normally, humans possess 23 pairs or 46 chromosomes in somatic (body) cells. Of the 23 pairs, 22 are identical in males and females. These 22 pairs are termed the **autosomal** chromosomes. The 23rd pair, referred to as the *sex chromosomes,* on the other hand, is very different in the two sexes. In males, this pair is characterized by one large and one small chromosome, termed the X and the Y, respectively. In females, two X chromosomes comprise the 23rd pair.

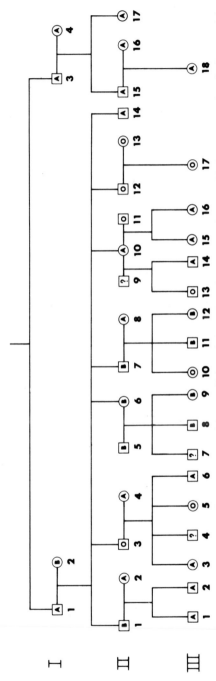

Figure 2.10. Pedigree of a family segregating for the alleles of the ABO blood group locus. This is an example of a locus with multiple alleles. Adapted from Jameson, R. S., et al. Nail-Patella Syndrome: clinical and linkage data on family G. *Annals of Human Genetics* 20. p. 349. Copyright © 1956 Cambridge University Press.

33

Since males have *two different sex chromosomes* (heterogametic) the sperm will be of two types, X-bearing and Y-bearing, produced in equal frequencies. Females, with the *same sex chromosomes* (homogametic), can produce only X-bearing eggs.[7] Thus, male parents transmit only the Y chromosome from the 23rd pair to their male offspring and the X chromosome to their female offspring. Females always transmit an X chromosome from this pair to their offspring. If genes that determine traits other than sexual characteristics are located on either the X or Y chromosome, the pattern of inheritance should be readily discernible because of the association with sex.

An example of a sex-linked trait is hemophilia A, an abnormality of blood clotting also known as the "bleeder's" disease. The gene responsible for this abnormality is carried by the X chromosome (X-linked) and is recessive to the allele determining normal blood clotting. The pedigree in Figure 2.11 illustrates the inheritance of hemophilia A.

The first and most striking aspect of this pedigree is that *only* males exhibit hemophilia. Why should this occur if the trait is X-linked? First, the trait is recessive. As we saw before, individuals must be *homozygous* recessive to express a trait controlled by recessive alleles. However, males have only one X chromosome and therefore cannot be homozygous. Thus, it is apparent that only *one* of the X chromosomes is necessary for the expression of the trait. The new term we shall employ to describe this condition is **hemizygous**. Males are hemizygous (have only one copy of the gene) for all X-linked traits.

As with most of the other traits seen thus far, hemophilia A is rare, so most individuals would be expected to be heterozygotes. This is true for females, but since males carry only one X chromosome they cannot be heterozygotes. They either have hemophilia or they don't.

The expression of hemophilia A *commonly* results from transmission of the gene from a heterozygous mother, who doesn't express hemophilia, to her son, who would thus be hemizygous and a hemophiliac. This holds true because the only way for a female offspring to express hemophilia is for her father to be hemophiliac *and* for her mother to be either heterozygous or herself a hemophiliac. However, hemophilia A is a severe disease and until recently the bleeding was hard to control. This results in high mortality of individuals with hemophilia. Therefore, matings in which one parent had hemophilia A would have been rare. Thus, the most common transmission of hemophilia is from an unaffected, heterozygous female, who mates with an unaffected male, to her sons.

---

[7]The gametes (eggs and sperm) carry only one of each pair of chromosomes; each then has 23 chromosomes, one of each pair. Thus the offspring, the result of gametic union, will have 46 chromosomes.

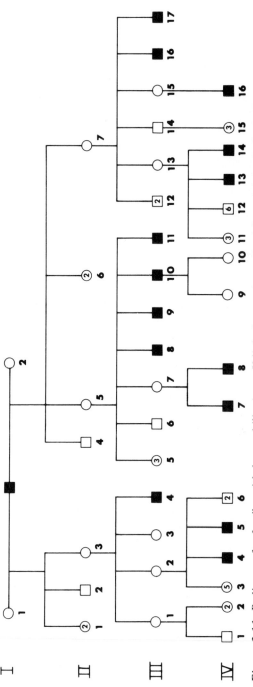

Figure 2.11. Pedigree of a family with hemophilia A, an X-linked recessive trait. Adapted from Bullock, W., and Fildes, P. Haemophilia. *Treasury of Human Inheritance* 1. Pedigree 490. Copyright © 1911 Cambridge University Press.

Females, who receive one X chromosome from their fathers, will in all cases be heterozygous for hemophilia A if their fathers are hemophiliac and their mothers homozygous dominant. If the mother is heterozygous, 50% of her daughters are expected to be heterozygous and 50% homozygous recessive hemophiliacs. By contrast, males with hemophiliac fathers and homozygous dominant mothers will never exhibit hemophilia A because they receive only the Y chromosome from their father. These circumstances explain why the pattern of inheritance often appears as being from mother to son and from father to daughter, but never father to son or, solely, mother to daughter.

Because this trait is controlled by a recessive allele it can skip generations or remain hidden for many generations, being carried by females and by chance not transmitted to males. If the males do not receive this allele they won't express the trait *and* they won't pass it on to their descendants; for the trait to appear it must be reintroduced by a female or a hemophiliac male. This is the general pattern of inheritance seen for all rare, X-linked recessive alleles.

In addition to traits determined by X-linked recessive alleles, there is strong evidence that some human traits are controlled by X-linked dominant alleles. One of the most likely is the condition known as X-linked vitamin D resistant rickets. As the name implies, individuals with this allele have rickets and are resistant to normal dosages of vitamin D.

In a very large pedigree spanning many generations, 7 affected males produced 21 offspring, in which all 11 females were affected and all 10 males were unaffected. This is precisely what is expected if the trait is X-linked—father to daughter transmission. Since the trait is dominant, the females need only be heterozygous to express it. If this trait were an autosomal dominant, then we would expect 50% of *all* offspring, both males and females, to be affected.

The opposite (*reciprocal*) matings of the affected females and their unaffected mates produced approximately 50% affected offspring of both sexes. This ratio of offspring would be expected as a result of a simple dominant where all females are heterozygous. However, since the affected males and unaffected females produced offspring in a ratio perfectly fitted to that expected on the basis of an X-linked dominant, it appears that vitamin D-resistant rickets is actually such a trait.

When considering X-linked dominants, we can still observe the father to daughter transmission but we must also be aware of the possibility of mother to daughter transmission. Thus, the critical "test" which shows that an allele is an X-linked dominant is that matings between unaffected females and affected males will produce only affected females and unaffected males.

While there is overwhelming evidence of the existence of X-linked genes, there is little evidence (and even this is equivocal) for Y-linked genes other than those that are sex determiners. We shall discuss the possibility of a trait being controlled by Y-linked genes: hairy ear rims.

Since only males possess the Y chromosome, Y-linked traits should only be expressed by males and always be transmitted from father to son. The best evidence for a Y-linked gene other than one determining a male sexual characteristic involves the gene controlling hairy ear rims. This trait is expressed as long, rigid hairs on the ears. Some pedigrees show that every male possessing the same Y chromosome (the Y chromosome from a common male ancestor with hairy ear rims) exhibits hairy ear rims while in other pedigrees some males possessing the same Y chromosome do not have hairy ear rims and some do. If the gene controlling this character is Y-linked, then we must explain why some individuals who have the same Y chromosome and thus the same gene do not express the same trait.

Although we shall discuss the concept of variable expression of traits in the last section, some factors that appear to affect the expression of hairy ear rims will be presented here. Age appears to be one such factor. Elder men in a family or a population in which the trait is present always show a higher frequency of hairy ear rims than do younger men. Thus, some males in various pedigrees that have been classified as not having hairy ear rims might not have been old enough to express the gene. Also, different families appear to possess different alleles at the locus on the Y chromosome controlling hairy ear rims (multiple allelism). Some of the alleles cause a very slight expression of the trait while others cause a very strong expression. As we shall see, age dependence and variation in "strength" of expression are common occurrences in many genetically controlled traits.

chapter three

MOLECULAR GENETICS
AND GENE ACTION

In the last section we saw examples of human traits transmitted according to Mendel's laws. Many of these characteristics can be explored further and the products of the genes, which control the traits, can be observed. As we shall see, the gene controlling a trait does not itself produce, for example, red blood cells that are sickled or an entirely unpigmented individual. Rather, the genes produce substances which then, as a result of their actions and/or inter-actions with other gene products, act to determine the trait. The present section will briefly discuss the structure and chemical characteristics of the genetic material as well as gene products and how these products act to produce traits.

Nucleic Acids

As early as 1866, a biologist named Ernst Haeckel proposed that the cell nucleus, containing the chromosomes, was the principal agent in inheritance. In the quest for establishing the chemical identity of the material controlling heredity Friedrich Miescher in 1869 developed a method for extracting the nucleus from cells. Chemical analysis of the nucleus showed that it was composed of, among other substances, an acidic compound termed *nuclein* which is characterized by large amounts of phosphorus. At that time nuclein was considered an oddity in that it was unprecedented and thus could not be compared with other compounds.

In the 1880s many investigators accepted Haeckel's proposal and went one step further by implying that the chromosomes were the actual hereditary bodies. However, when somatic cells divide the chromosomes *double* and are distributed to each new cell. Thus, when fertilization occurs there must be a reduction in chromosome number in the sex cells in order for the offspring to maintain the normal chromosome complement of the species. This theoretical aspect of cell division led to investigations, in both plants and animals, of sex cell production (*gametogenesis*). It was found that there was a mechanism of cell division that reduced the chromosome number in the gametes. This reduction division was termed *meiosis*. The ultimate result of meiotic cell divisions is the gametes (eggs and sperm), each with half the number of chromosomes that characterize the species.

In addition to investigations of cell mechanisms producing gametes, the chemical makeup of the nuclei of gametes was also studied. Discoveries showed that nuclein was present in association with various proteins. This combination became known as nucleoprotein. The two types of protein most often associated with nuclein were protamine, found in fish sperm, and histones, generally found in other cell nuclei. Protamine is quite simple in structure, whereas the histones are rather complex. The question then arose which of the three compounds, nuclein, protamine, or histone, was the genetic material.

Because of the great diversity of organisms and the manifold functions performed by each organism, it was thought that the genetic material must be capable of bearing a great amount of information and thus be rather complex. In addition, since the genetic material governs all traits in individuals, its presence must be constant in all cells. Of the three nuclear compounds considered, histones are the most complex but are not present in all cells (they are absent, for example, from fish sperm), protamine is a very simple compound but also is not present in all cells, and nuclein is a constant feature of all cells and is much more complex than thought at first. Nuclein was therefore considered by some to be the best candidate for the genetic material.

The search for the genetic material continued into the second decade of the 20th century with some investigators favoring proteins and some favoring nuclein, or nucleic acid, as it came to be known. From 1925 to 1930 P. Levene showed that nucleic acid, after separation from protein, could be broken down into smaller fractions termed **nucleotides**. The nucleotides were composed of three parts: a sugar, a phosphate group (noted by Miescher), and a portion that contained nitrogen. The sugar portion of nucleic acid could be of two types, although each contained five carbon atoms. The two sugar portions were termed *ribose* and *deoxyribose,* the latter differing from ribose

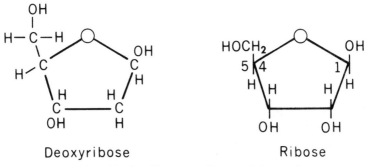

Deoxyribose   **Ribose**

Figure 3.1. Nucleotide sugars ribose and deoxyribose.

only by lacking one oxygen atom. The structures of these sugars are presented in Figure 3.1.

Even though there are two types of sugars, specific nucleic acids contain only one type. Nucleic acids can be subdivided into two classes based on the sugar present: ribonucleic acid (**RNA**), with the sugar ribose, and deoxyribonucleic acid (**DNA**), with the sugar deoxyribose. RNA is commonly found outside the cell nucleus while DNA is almost exclusively found in the nucleus.

A constant component of each class of nucleic acid is the phosphate group. This group is attached to the sugar molecules at the number 5 carbon atom and is acidic in nature.

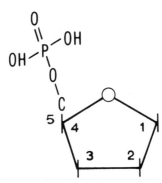

Figure 3.2. Attachment of phosphate group to nucleotide sugar at number 5 carbon atom.

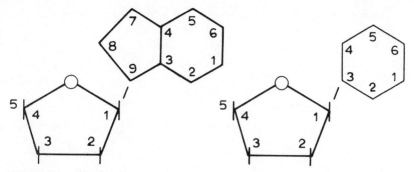

Figure 3.3. Attachment of nitrogen-containing base of nucleotide sugar at number 1 carbon.

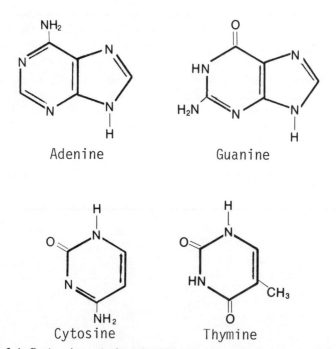

Adenine

Guanine

Cytosine

Thymine

Figure 3.4. Purine (two-ring) and pyrimidine (one-ring) bases. Adenine (A), guanine (G), cytosine (C), and thymine (T) are found in DNA. Uracil (U) replaces thymine in RNA. (From Hill, J. W. *Chemistry for changing times.* 2nd ed. Minneapolis: Burgess Publishing Co. Copyright © 1975.

The final component of nucleotides, the nitrogen-containing portion, is the most variable. This component is attached to the number 1 carbon atom of the sugar molecule and can be either a one- or a two-ring structure. The single-ring structures are called *pyrimidines,* and the two-ring structures *purines.*

RNA and DNA also differ in the kinds of pyrimidines present. RNA commonly contains the pyrimidines cytosine and uracil while DNA has cytosine and thymine. Both RNA and DNA, however, contain the same purines, adenine and guanine. The structures of these bases are shown in Figure 3.4.

Thus, nucleotides can be of two classes based on the sugar present: ribonucleotides and deoxyribonucleotides. Each class of nucleotide can be further distinguished by the nitrogen-containing bases.

Additional studies indicated that the nucleotides were linked together to form chains. For example, Levene found that a DNA chain was structured as shown in Figure 3.5.

Levene also found that, in DNA, the four kinds of deoxyribonucleotides were present in equal amounts and joined in small chains of about four nucleotides each. Later, in the 1940s, it was found that DNA is actually present in very long chains composed of thousands of joined nucleotides. Levene in his investigations unwittingly broke up the larger chains. In addition, it was found that the nucleotide bases were not necessarily present in equal amounts but were present according to the ratio (adenine + cystosine) = (thymine + guanine). This ratio suggested a paired relationship between the bases.

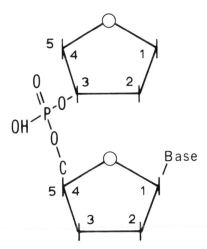

Figure 3.5. The 3-to-5 linkage of nucleotide sugars via the phosphate group.

43

Levene's work indicated that DNA, like protamine, was a rather simple molecule and was not complex enough to explain the great diversity in living organisms. Thus, little work was done with DNA for some time.

During the period Levene was investigating the structure of DNA, Frank Griffith in 1928 also conducted a series of experiments that apply to our present discussion. Griffith's experiments essentially consisted of injecting non-virulent and virulent bacteria into mice and noting the effect. For example, mice injected with a nonvirulent bacterial strain do not perish. When the virulent strain is heated and killed and then injected into mice, again the mice do not perish. However, when heat-killed, virulent bacteria are injected into mice previously injected with the nonvirulent bacteria, the mice die and virulent bacteria are found within them. This suggests that there has been a *transformation* of some substance in the nonvirulent bacteria by virulent bacteria.

The identity of the transforming agent was unknown and the search for it began. In 1944 D. T. Avery, C. M. MacLeod, and M. McCarthy performed experiments somewhat similar to Griffith's and found the transforming agent. The investigation of Avery, MacLeod, and McCarthy can be divided into three parts: (1) nonvirulent bacteria were added to a culture medium and allowed to reproduce; only nonvirulent bacteria were found; (2) DNA from virulent but heat-killed bacteria was added to a culture medium; no bacteria were found; (3) nonvirulent bacteria and DNA from heat-killed, virulent bacteria were added to a culture medium that could keep virulent and nonvirulent bacteria separate. After a growth period both virulent and nonvirulent bacteria were found on the medium. These results indicated very strongly that DNA is the transforming agent. Because one organism can cause traits of another to be changed, this also points to DNA as the genetic material.

Also in the 1940s, as mentioned on page 43, additional information on the structure of DNA was obtained. DNA was found, in fact, to be present as a very long chainlike molecule, with the links connected in the way shown by Levene (Figure 3.5). This finding indicated that because DNA was long it could be complex enough to contain all the messages required for the biological composition of an organism. Since there is a possibility of four different nucleotide bases at each position of the DNA chain, much variability or complexity could be attained simply by heterogeneous placement of the bases along the chain. If each of the four DNA bases (thymine, guanine, cytosine, and adenine) were a message, then only four characters could be produced. However, if two adjacent bases made up the message, then 4^2 or 16 messages could be contained in DNA. Similarly, if three or four or five adjacent bases made up the code, then 4^3 or 64, 4^4 or 256, and 4^5 or 1024 different messages could be contained. As you probably have seen, the number of possible

44

messages increases exponentially. The general expression is 4^n, where n equals the numbers of bases that together contain the message. By increasing n, extremely large numbers of messages are possible.

Thus by the 1940s there was much evidence suggesting that DNA, both in structure and function, was the genetic material.

After the work of Avery, MacLeod, and McCarthy many additional transformation experiments were successfully conducted in bacteria and a number of traits could be transferred between individual strains. In addition to these experiments on bacteria, an important experiment was conducted involving viruses. In 1952 A. O. Hershey and M. Chase investigated the mechanism by which a specific type of virus, a bacteriophage, infected and ultimately destroyed (lysed) bacteria. It was known at this time that the bacteriophage, if ruptured, yielded two main fractions: small DNA particles and protein structures. If the protein structures alone were attached to bacteria, the bacteria would be destroyed but no new viruses would be formed. Only when both DNA and the protein were present would new viruses be produced.

Hershey and Chase proposed to examine the fate of the DNA and protein fractions when the virus infected bacteria. To do this they "labeled" the DNA of viruses by growing them with radioactive phosphorus, ^{32}P. They also labeled the protein by the addition of radioactive sulphur, ^{35}S. This procedure could be used to show where DNA and protein could be found after infection of the bacteria because DNA has phosphorus and no sulphur whereas proteins have sulphur and no phosphorus. They then permitted either ^{32}P-labeled viruses or ^{35}S-labeled viruses to infect the bacteria. The viruses recovered from the bacteria (which were the offspring of the infecting virus) contained only ^{32}P, indicating that DNA was passed from parent to offspring. Later experiments have also shown that DNA is the material passed to the viral offspring.

The Watson-Crick Model

More and more evidence was accumulating which pointed to DNA as the genetic material. But what exactly was DNA and how did it function? As we have seen, by the 1940s the nucleotide chain structure, or the *primary structure*, of DNA was established. The next line of investigation focused on the arrangement of the chain or possibly chains of DNA. Evidence indicating that the DNA chain was not a single structure came from the relationship of the bases ($[A + C] = [T + G]$), which suggested a paired structure, and from X-ray studies of crystalized DNA, which suggested a multiple-chain structure. In 1953 Watson and Crick, synthesizing the information concerning DNA structure, proposed the double helix model of DNA. They showed that DNA

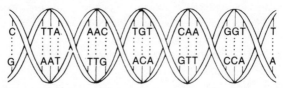

Figure 3.6. A representation of the helix of DNA. From Hill, J. W. *Chemistry for changing times.* 2nd ed. Minneapolis: Burgess Publishing Co. Copyright © 1975.

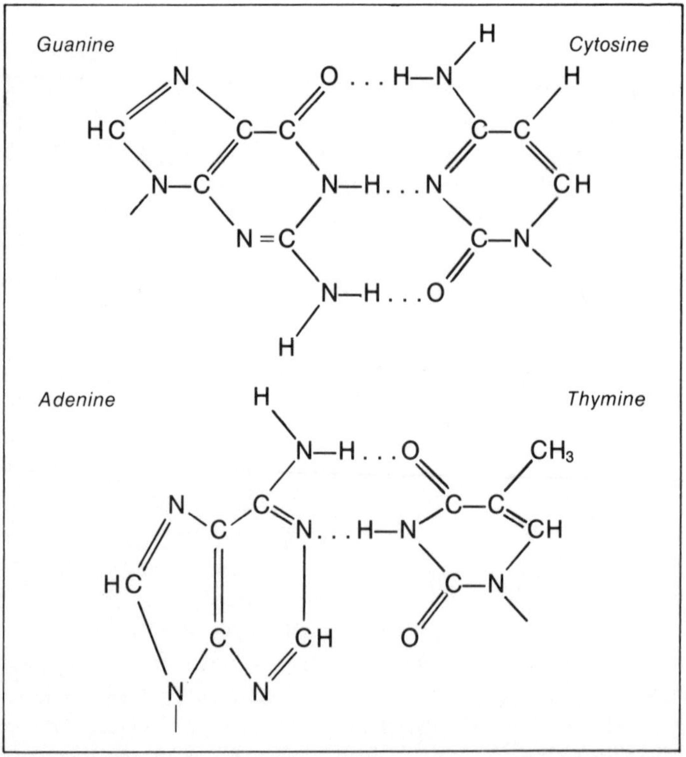

Figure 3.7. Base pairing in the DNA double helix. From Hill, J. W. *Chemistry for changing times.* 2nd ed. Minneapolis: Burgess Publishing Co. Copyright © 1975.

is a *double-stranded* molecule, with each strand coiled around the other in a manner similar to the coiling of a rope. The structure of the coil is *helical,* as a spiral staircase, with the stairs always of the same length and the entire structure with the same diameter.

The chemical structure of the "staircase" can be pictured as follows. Each strand of DNA comprises about half of the staircase, with each strand consisting of half a step and one railing. The steps, chemically, are the bases adenine, cytosine, thymine, and guanine, and the railing consists of the phosphate groups which link the nucleotides. When the two strands are joined the staircase arrangement is attained. In the joined structure, the "steps," which are in pairs commonly called **base pairs,** connect each half.

By proposing this structure for DNA, Watson and Crick imposed *physical limits* to the dimension of the structure. They found that *only* when each base pair consisted of one purine and one pyrimidine would the "stairs" of the helix be equal in length and fit together. Further, the structures of the purines and the pyrimidines determined that adenine would bond only with thymine and cytosine only with guanine. Thus, in analyzing the relative amounts of the bases, an investigator should find the relationships A = T and G = C or, in another form, (A + G) = (C + T). We have seen that this relationship had already been found. The proposed structure of DNA and the pairing of the bases are illustrated in Figures 3.6 and 3.7.

The arrangement of the base pairs shows that the strands are *complementary,* that is, the structure of one strand must be composed of bases that will "fit" into the other strand. Thus, if one strand has bases ···ATGCA··· the other will have bases ···TACGT··· at the same level.

Watson and Crick then proposed a mechanism by which DNA could replicate (duplicate) itself. Replication is obviously a necessary requirement of the genetic material because, when a cell divides, two new but exact copies are usually the result. To replicate, the DNA of the Watson-Crick model has only to unwind at two points and then each strand may attract nucleotides with complementary bases. Since each old strand is the complement of the other, the replicates of *each* old strand, the new strands, are identical to the complementary old strand. Thus, the new DNA molecule, according to the model, should consist of an old strand and a new complementary strand. This type of replication is termed semiconservative and is contrasted with the *conservative* replication in which both old strands would each make a new strand and the two new strands would make up one DNA molecule and the old strands would make up the other.

In 1958 Meselson and Stahl tested the hypothesis of semiconservative replication in DNA. In this experiment bacteria were grown on a medium that contained heavy nitrogen (^{15}N) as the *only* source of nitrogen. After many generations the DNA of bacteria grown with the heavy nitrogen contained only ^{15}N and was thus heavier than DNA in which normal nitrogen, ^{14}N, was present. When cells containing DNA with only ^{15}N were grown on a medium containing only ^{14}N, the DNA of the offspring was lighter than the DNA containing only ^{15}N but heavier than DNA containing only ^{14}N.[1] The second generation of bacteria grown on an unlabeled medium showed two types of DNA: one type was characterized as containing only ^{14}N and the other was similar to that found in the first generation. The third generation showed two types of DNA, but the heavier type was even less frequent than the lighter type. If replication of DNA were conservative, DNA containing only ^{15}N should be present every generation. The results of Meselson and Stahl indicate that this is not the case. The very first generation grown with normal ^{14}N shows DNA of only one kind—the kind intermediate in weight between ^{15}N DNA and ^{14}N DNA. This is just what is expected if replication is semiconservative. Generations 2 and 3 also conform to the semiconservative replication hypothesis since exclusive ^{15}N DNA is never found. The experiments of Meselson and Stahl, as well as others, do indicate that DNA replication is semiconservative.

Experiments observing the replication of chromosomes also indicate a semiconservative mechanism. Taylor and his associates found that cells of a bean plant after being grown in the presence of a radioactive form of thymine exhibit chromosomes that are half labeled and half unlabeled in a way similar to the results of Meselson and Stahl.

RNA

Earlier in this section mention was made of a second nucleic acid, RNA. As was noted, RNA differs from DNA in that RNA contains the sugar ribose as opposed to deoxyribose in DNA, RNA contains the pyrimidine uracil as opposed to thymine in DNA, and RNA can be found generally throughout the cell while DNA is almost totally restricted to the nucleus. In higher organisms RNA is produced by DNA in a manner analogous to the way DNA replicates itself, that is, a strand of DNA serves as a template and complementary bases are then put together in a sequence provided by the DNA. However, this mechanism differs from the replication of DNA in that the base uracil pairs with adenine (of the DNA) so that the RNA will contain uracil, not thymine. Also, RNA is the complement of only one strand of DNA and thus is itself single stranded.

RNA of higher organisms plays a fundamental role in the production of proteins (for example, hemoglobin). RNA can be divided by function into

---

[1]The two types of DNA were separated by centrifugation.

three groups: mRNA, rRNA, and tRNA. The first RNA we shall consider is mRNA, or messenger RNA. As the name implies, this type of RNA carries a message; specifically it carries the code it has obtained from DNA for the structure of a protein. Proteins are constructed from a number of building blocks termed *amino acids*[2] and the mRNA codes for these. Proteins are assembled from amino acids through **translation** of information coded in mRNA. But how are the amino acids brought to the correct mRNA? This is the function of tRNA, or transfer RNA. This type of RNA obtains amino acids and transfers them to the mRNA. Transfer RNA is able to carry and transfer the "correct" amino acid (that is, the one coded for by the DNA and whose message is carried by mRNA) because tRNA has a code that is complementary to the mRNA. Each tRNA carries one amino acid and is transferred to the site on mRNA for which it has the complementary code. The process of transfer occurs on specific cellular structures called ribosomes. The ribosomes hold the mRNA and the tRNA's and allow the process of protein synthesis to occur. The third RNA, rRNA or ribosomal RNA, is a constituent part of the ribosomes. In the next section we shall explore this mechanism further.

Gene Action

In higher organisms there is overwhelming evidence that DNA carries the genetic code, that is, the messages that control which traits will be expressed by an individual. How does the message, somehow contained in the nucleotides, produce a trait? First we shall look at the nature of the messages and then explore somewhat the means used in translating the messages.

The function of the genetic material is to control and produce various traits in an individual (phenotype). However, intervening between the genetic material and the trait are a vast number of complex steps making the elucidation of the process difficult. Nevertheless, some information concerning this process is available. In 1941, Beadle and Tatum, working with the mold *Neurospora*, arrived at the conclusion that many genes are primarily responsible for the production of specific proteins called enzymes.[3] This is usually referred to as the *one gene-one enzyme* concept, which encompasses the following: (1) biochemical pathways in organisms can be subdivided into separate steps; (2) each of these steps is governed by the action of a specific

[2] See pages 50 and 51 for a fuller discussion.

[3] Enzymes are biochemical catalysts which enable various reactions to occur. A simple example is digestion, in which enzymes combine with ingested food and break it down into its constituent parts, which are then used by the body for such processes as growth and repair.

enzyme; (3) each of these enzymes is controlled by a gene; and (4) the alteration of a gene results only in the change of an enzyme and thus only in the way a single step of the pathway is carried out. The alteration of genes is a type of *mutation* (mutations, which will not be discussed in detail, can be thought of as any *changes* in the genetic material, the most obvious being those changes that result in new traits being produced.) As was later found, this general concept of one gene-one enzyme held not only for *Neurospora* but also for humans and a variety of other organisms. The genetic material thus seems to be intimately associated with the production of proteins. How is this accomplished? We have already seen a general outline of the process when discussing the types of RNA. Now we shall explore the matter further, starting with the nature of proteins and the genetic code itself.

Proteins and the Genetic Code _____

In the early part of the 19th century, H. Braconnot, a French chemist, subjected the protein gelatin to heat and acid. The product of this reaction was a crystal which tasted sweet. The name given to this molecule was glycine (from the Greek meaning sweet). The structure of this molecule was found (Figure 3.8) and was seen to be very simple. A carbon atom is attached to both an amine group and a carboxylic acid group. Molecules of this general type are termed amino acids. They are the basic constituents of proteins. If all proteins were as simple as gelatin, which is composed of linked glycine molecules, they would be relatively simple in structure and function. However, not all proteins are made only of glycine. Braconnot isolated from a second protein a white crystal composed of an amino acid called leucine (from the Greek meaning white).

As you can see in Figure 3.9, leucine, although of the same general makeup as glycine, is more complex because of the large side chain. From the initial isolation of the simplest amino acid, glycine, in the early 19th century, additional amino acids have been found by the breakdown of proteins. The

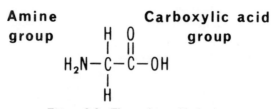

Figure 3.8. The amino acid glycine.

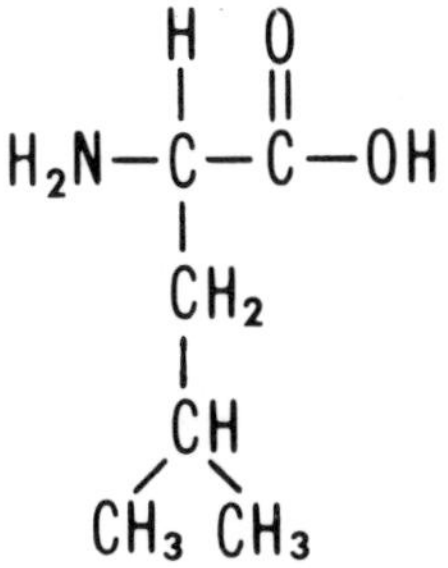

Figure 3.9. The amino acid leucine.

number of known amino acids now stands at 22. Of these, 21 occur in almost all proteins and the other is found principally in only one protein. As with the difference between glycine and leucine, the various amino acids are characterized by different side chains. However, another significant aspect of the amino acids is their diversity. Proteins, in contrast to other large molecules in living organisms, are made up of the largest number of subunits—amino acids. Thus, proteins may be of the most complex nature.

But how does DNA, with only four variable subunits (A, C, G, T) code for a protein? We have already seen that the number of messages contained by DNA can be very large if more than one base pair codes for the message (see page 44). Since there are more than 16 types of amino acids in proteins we can postulate that more than 2 base pairs (4^2 = 16) code for each amino acid. If three base pairs make up a single code word, there are 64 possible words (4^3 = 64). We can use this possibility as a starting point and investigate its ramifications for coding. If three bases do in fact code for 1 amino acid, it appears that 44 of these triplets or **codons** are unnecessary since only 20 amino acids need to be coded.[4] What is the function of these 44 "extra" codons? Some or all could be punctuation marks in the messages. Another possibility is that more than one codon carry the same message, that is, they code for the same amino acid. Codes in which different elements (in this case the codons or triplets) contain the same message are termed *degenerate*. These codes should be contrasted with *ambiguous* codes in which the same element codes different messages. The latter type of code does not seem in keeping with the precision witnessed in living organisms. In addition to the size of the codon, the format for "reading" the codon must be considered.

[4] Only 20 amino acids will be considered to be directly coded by DNA. The remaining amino acids seem to be derived, secondarily, from two coded amino acids.

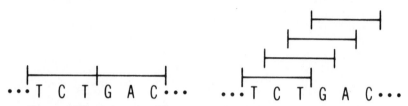
Figure 3.10. Codons 'read' as nonoverlapping and overlapping codes.

For example, are the codons read in an overlapping or nonoverlapping manner (Figure 3.10). The evidence of Beadle and Tatum as well as of others indicates that a change in a single gene or the change in a single nucleotide affects only one protein, and, further, only one amino acid in the protein. Thus, the code appears to be read in a *nonoverlapping* manner.

The length of the codon and other attributes of the genetic code were elucidated by Francis Crick and his associates in 1961. By inserting and/or deleting numbers of nucleotide bases in viruses they accumulated evidence that the code itself was degenerate, had no punctuation, and was very likely a triplet code. Also in 1961 Nirenberg and Matthaei showed that mRNA was necessary for protein synthesis. Using this finding they synthetically produced a small ribonucleotide containing only uracil. When this poly-U ribonucleotide was added to a protein synthesis system a small protein (polypeptide chain) was obtained which strikingly contained only one amino acid—phenylalanine! Thus, the *codon* carried by mRNA which specified the amino acid phenylalanine was UUU. The *anticodon,* carried by tRNA (which bears the amino acids and transfer them to the mRNA) must then be AAA. Using this method, Nirenberg and his coworkers tested all 64 triplets and found that all 20 amino acids were produced. The code was found to be as shown in Table 3.1.

To quickly summarize these findings we have seen that (1) DNA contains the messages for the coding of proteins; (2) each message is transcribed through the process called **transcription** to mRNA which carries the message to the site of protein synthesis, the ribosomes, which contain rRNA; and (3) tRNA carries amino acids to the mRNA.

Each tRNA has a specific anticodon (which is complementary to the codon) and in turn carries only the amino acid that is called for by the codon of the mRNA. In this manner amino acids are built into very long chains or proteins. Is this process controlled somehow or are all proteins continuously being manufactured by all cells? Simply by observing living organisms we can see that certain parts of the organism are specialized for certain functions, such as digestion and formation of blood. Since most of the specialized functions depend on different proteins, it appears that there are controls which allow only certain proteins to be produced by certain cells. We shall now look at a simple control mechanism which operates in bacteria.

Gene Regulation

In 1961 F. Jacob and J. Monod presented a paper on mechanisms of genetic regulation. This work, and subsequently many others, have focused on mechanisms which control protein synthesis. These studies have suggested four main components in the control of gene action. These four components may be termed an **operon**: (1) a gene or a group of genes which has its activity regulated; (2) an **operator** gene or region of DNA at one end of the gene or group of genes, which is responsive to a regulator protein or which produces a regulator-responsive molecule; (3) the regulator protein; and (4) a **regulator gene** for regulator proteins. A very simplified model of these relationships is presented in Figure 3.11.

Table 3.1. The Genetic Code

First Letter	Second Letter				Third Letter
	U	C	A	G	
U	phe	ser	tyr	cys	U
	phe	ser	tyr	cys	C
	leu	ser	(1)*[a]	(3)*	A
	leu	ser	(2)*	trp	G
C	leu	pro	his	arg	U
	leu	pro	his	arg	C
	leu	pro	gen	arg	A
	leu	pro	gen	arg	G
A	ile	thr	asn	ser	U
	ile	thr	asn	ser	C
	ile	thr	lys	arg	A
	met	thr	lys	arg	G
G	val	ala	asp	gly	U
	val	ala	asp	gly	C
	val	ala	glu	gly	A
	val	ala	glu	gly	G

[a](1)*, (2)*, and (3)* are stop codes.

Table 3.1 shows that the code is triplet in nature, is degenerate (different triplets contain same message), and that punctuations do occur but are of the type analogous to periods, that is, they end messages but do not interrupt messages with pauses or commas.

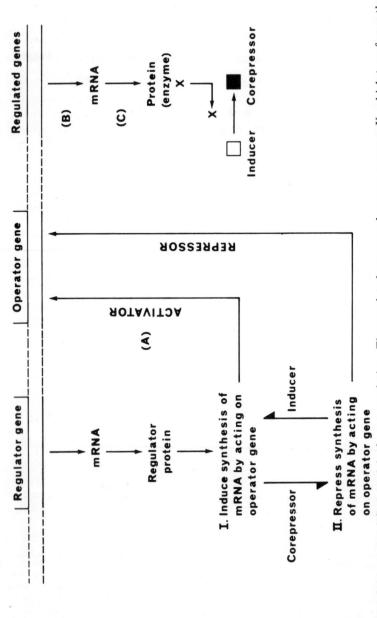

Figure 3.11. A simplified model of gene regulation. The regulated gene produces an enzyme, X, which transforms the substance represented by an open square to the substance represented by the darkened square. Adapted from Jacob, F., and Monod, F. Genetic regulatory mechanisms and the synthesis of proteins. *Journal of Molecular Biology* 3. p. 318. Copyright © 1961.

In this simplified model the regulator gene is seen to produce a regulator protein via mRNA. The regulator protein, in turn, may act in two ways. First, it may act on the operator to activate protein synthesis (Step A). When this occurs, mRNA from the gene(s) coding for an enzyme is produced (Step B), and finally the enzyme is synthesized (Step C). A second function of the regulator protein is repression of the synthesis of the enzyme. The regulator protein is transformed from an **activator** to a repressor by metabolites (**corepressors**) from the reaction controlled by the enzyme. When the reaction has proceeded and the end products have been produced, these end products then in turn transform the activator to the repressor and halt the production of the enzyme. This feedback insures that the enzyme will not be produced when it is not needed. However, when metabolites are present that must be broken down by the enzyme, these may act as **inducers** to transform the repressor back to an activator. Thus, the metabolic reaction controlled by the enzyme will continue until the end products (corepressors) accumulate and cause the regulator to become a repressor. In this way the enzyme is produced only when needed and energy is conserved. This very simplified model, based on studies in bacteria, may give some idea of the control of gene action.

The above discussion shows that the one gene-one enzyme hypothesis must be modified somewhat since all genes do not necessarily produce enzymes. We may now alter this hypothesis to a one gene (or one specific segment of DNA)-one polypeptide hypothesis.

We shall now move one step further and explore how the products of the genes, specifically enzymes, may act and interact to produce traits that are visible to experimenters. In this discussion the concept of dominance will again be explored—and redefined.

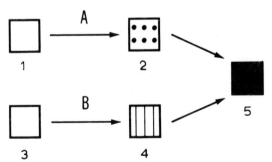

Figure 3.12. Two metabolic pathways governed by two independent loci. The final phenotype, 5, represents the combination of the two independent traits 2 and 4. For example, phenotype 5 may represent smooth, yellow seeds as in Mendel's experiments.

If we return for a moment to Mendel's experiments with two factors, each one affecting a different trait, we should remember that the ratio of offspring found in the F$_2$ generation was 9:3:3:1. We may now view this ratio in terms of the metabolic pathways that are responsible for the production of substances that affect the traits. For simplicity, the pathways may be represented as in Figure 3.12, where gene A converts substance 1 to substance 2, and gene B converts substance 3 to substance 4. The presence of gene a (recessive allele of A) blocks the first reaction so only 1 is present while b (recessive allele of B) blocks the second reaction and only 3 is present. When both A and B are present we shall consider the phenotype as the combination

AABB   X   aabb

F$_1$ AaBb

Figure 3.13. A cross between individuals possessing genes governing the reaction in Figure 3.12.

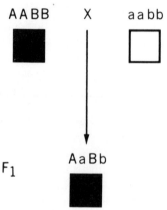

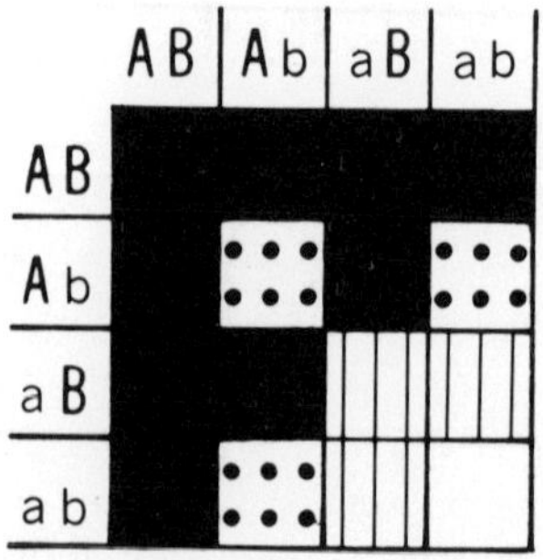

Figure 3.14. The expected F$_2$ generation resulting from the cross of F$_1$ individuals in Figure 3.13.

56

of both shown in number 5 of Figure 3.12. Thus the cross shown in Figure 3.13 will produce an F_2 all of phenotype 5.

These F_1 individuals when self-fertilized (or mated with other F_1 individuals) produce an F_2 of the ratio 9 $A\_B\_$: 3 A_bb: 3 $aaB\_$: 1 $aabb$.

This ratio results when two genes, each affecting a different trait (via a different metabolic pathway), act independently and A and B are dominant to a and b, respectively. But what will occur when the two genes act on the same trait via the same pathway? We can represent the pathway as in Figure 3.15.

In this pathway aa or bb blocks the pathway and the final product, and the trait is therefore not produced. If the matings are the same as in Figure 3.13 all F_1 individuals will be able to produce the end product. In the F_2 generation, however, 9/16 will be able to produce the end product and 7/16 will not. This 9:7 ratio consists of 9 $A\_B\_$ individuals and 7 $AAbb$ or $aaB\_$ or $aabb$ individuals. If the A_bb and $aaB\_$ individuals differ, that is, if the pathway produces the products shown in Figure 3.16, the same cross will produce an F_2 ratio of 9 $A\_B\_$ individuals, who can produce the final product, 3 A_bb individuals, who can produce only the intermediate product, and 4 $aa\_\_$ individuals, who cannot produce the intermediate product and thus cannot produce the final product.

In addition to these F_2 ratios there are a number of other F_2 ratios that are obtained when the two gene pairs interact to produce phenotypes. The 9:3:4 ratio is an example of this type of interaction, which is termed *epistasis*,

Figure 3.15. A metabolic pathway governed by two independent loci. The dominant allele of each locus must be present for the production of the end product.

Figure 3.16. A metabolic pathway governed by two independent loci. The A allele is necessary for the production of the intermediate product and the B allele is necessary for the final product.

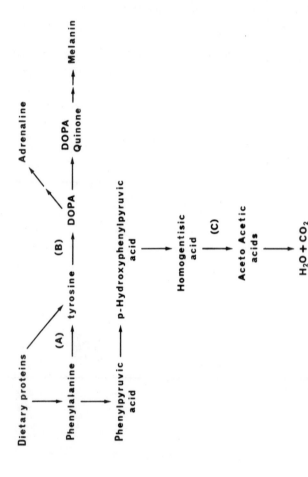

Figure 3.17. The metabolic pathway of the amino acids phenylalanine and tyrosine. The letter (A) represents the enzymatic alteration resulting in PKU, (B) the alteration resulting in albinism, and (C) the alteration resulting in alkaptonuria. Because of the interconnecting and rather complex nature of the metabolic pathways and the manifold effects various alleles can have on the pathways and ultimately the phenotype, only variations in (A) will be considered. However, the same type of investigation could be done when considering other traits and other pathways. The blocks at (B) and (C) could result in two of the conditions described by Garrod (albinism and alkaptonuria, respectively). Cystinuria and pentosuria result from blocked reactions in other pathways.

or the *phenomenon of one gene pair hiding the effects of another.* The epistatic interaction in the 9:3:4 ratio may be considered analogous to the dominance relationship between alleles since the presence of *aa* hides the effect of *B*. Another example of an epistatic relationship is the production of an F_2 ratio of 12:3:1. In this example *A* is dominant to *a*, *B* is dominant to *b*, and *A* is epistatic to both *B* and *b* (*A* hides the effect of either of these). Thus, the F_2 would consist of 12 *A_* (second gene pair hidden): 3 *aaB_*: 1 *aabb*. A pathway may be pictured again, as in Figure 3.16, where *A* blocks the first reaction and *B* blocks the second reaction.

We shall now return to the inheritance of human characteristics and explore the metabolic bases of a few. We shall initiate this discussion by examining a fairly well-known pathway and a result of its "malfunction": phenylketonuria.

Biochemical Basis of Some Inherited Disorders in Humans

The metabolic pathway of the amino acids phenylalanine and tryosine is shown in Figure 3.17. It has been found that if the enzyme (A) which converts phenylalanine to tyrosine is nonfunctional (or absent), the reaction (A) will not proceed and phenylalanine and its derivatives will increase in concentration in the body. Either phenylalanine or its derivatives in high concentrations are toxic to the central nervous system and their buildup almost always results in some form of mental retardation for the life of the person. Individuals who are unable to convert phenylalanine to tyrosine are said to have phenylketonuria or PKU. This genetic disease is inherited as a simple recessive, meaning that to show the trait individuals must be homozygous for the defective gene that causes the enzyme to be defective or absent. It follows then that the "normal" allele is dominant, so heterozygotes are indistinguishable from homozygous dominant individuals in appearance. However, with the elaboration of medical technology, it has become possible to distinguish, with some degree of accuracy, heterozygotes from homozygous dominant individuals. The test involves measuring the amount of phenylalanine in blood plasma. Since individuals with PKU lack the enzyme (phenylalanine hydroxylase) which converts phenylalanine to tyrosine, it follows that a buildup of phenylalanine is expected in these individuals with PKU. It has also been found that individuals heterozygous for PKU have generally higher concentrations of phenylalanine in blood plasma than homozygous dominants; however, there is some overlap between these genotypes. This example illustrates a difficulty in terminology based on the changing concept of gene action (and how we perceive it). Since PKU is the result of two alleles, it is generally thought of as a disease caused by recessive genes. However, since heterozygotes may be distinguished, it appears that the effects of *both* alleles may be seen in an individual; such a situation has been termed codominance.

This same discussion can be extended to the hemoglobin abnormality sickle cell anemia. (The biochemical basis of this condition is the alteration of a single amino acid in the β protein chain of hemoglobin. The alteration of the amino acid would itself be the result of the alteration of a single codon that codes for the amino acid.) Again, this disease is caused by the presence of two alleles and is generally considered a result of recessive genes, although heterozygotes can be distinguished and at times exhibit anemia. This is another example of the effect of both alleles being seen in the individual. To distinguish these conditions from codominance, which is usually applied to the case where the alleles contribute equally to the phenotype, the term *incomplete recessive* is used. This term indicates that although both alleles are needed to produce a trait, in heterozygotes the presence of only one can be distinguished. In an analogous way we can employ the term **incomplete dominant** for traits in which the heterozygotes are distinguishable from the homozygous dominants.[5] Both of these terms should convey the idea of the other. Thus, the concepts of dominant and recessive are not really properties of the genes. Rather, they are applied to alleles in order to describe the interaction between them; for example, their relative activities or their "ability" to influence the phenotype. Obviously, the definitions may change as a result of our ability to distinguish these allelic interactions.

We may now explore another facet of gene action—manifold effects of one gene, or pleiotropism. Again PKU will provide an excellent example.

Figure 3.17 shows the site in the metabolism of phenylalanine which is blocked in individuals with PKU. When levels of phenylalanine in blood plasma are compared between individuals with PKU (homozygous recessive) and "normal" or control individuals (homozygous dominant) two *distinct* distributions are formed with no overlap. Thus, one consequence of having PKU is exhibiting high levels of phenylalanine. Since large amounts of phenylalanine or its derivatives are toxic to the nervous system and result in some form of mental retardation, there should be some difference in the distribution of IQ's between individuals with PKU and controls. This is the case, but as opposed to the amount of phenylalanine in the blood plasma, there is some overlap in the distribution of IQ's (since PKU is not the only cause of retardation we may expect some of the individuals who do not have PKU—the

---

[5] Brachydactyly may be an incomplete dominant. There is evidence that matings between individuals with brachydactyly result in offspring who are stillborn or die shortly after birth and exhibit severe skeletal malformations, possibly the result of the effects of *both* dominant alleles.

controls—to show low IQ's). Thus, intelligence is a second trait affected by the gene. Finally, Figure 3.17 shows that the metabolic block resulting in PKU is in the same pathway which ultimately produces melanin, a color pigment. (Note that recessive albinism is caused, in some cases, by the block of the next step in this path.) Individuals with PKU produce less tyrosine and thus very often have light-colored hair and blue eyes, even when it is known they possess genes for darker coloration.[6] Here are two more traits affected by the gene(s).

The gene causing sickle cell anemia is also pleiotropic. Although the function of the gene involved is to produce the β chain of hemoglobin, the abnormal allele, when homozygous, results in such effects as jaundice, brain damage, degeneration of the spleen, short stature, and poor general development. These effects are for the most part due to the fact that the sickled red blood cells (containing Hb S) often clot in relatively small blood vessels, causing the tissues in an area to degenerate to some degree.

The concept of variable **expressivity** of genes (page 37) may be easily integrated into the present discussion. For example, the pleiotropic effects of the gene for PKU are variable. As was mentioned there is a *distribution* of amounts of phenylalanine in the blood plasma of individuals with PKU; that is, everyone with PKU shows a somewhat different amount of phenylalanine in the blood (although all have much greater amounts than "normal" individuals). Why is there variation if all individuals share the same genes at that locus? The answer in part may stem from the fact that these individuals do *not* share all of their other genes (the genetic background) nor do they share the same environmental situations. The kinds and amounts of *dietary* proteins, an environmental variable, may differ greatly among individuals, affecting the amount of phenylalanine present in blood plasma. Thus, individuals ingesting greater amounts of phenylalanine would be expected to have greater amounts in the blood plasma. In addition, other enzymes, controlled by other genes, may vary among these individuals. For example, the enzyme converting phenylalanine to phenylpyruvic acid may vary in form to some degree because its synthesis can be controlled by different alleles, with some forms performing this reaction either more rapidly or more efficiently than others. Thus, phenylalanine may be metabolized differently in the other pathways. These kinds of considerations, both genetic and environmental, may be expanded to include the other effects of the genes for PKU. In this manner, we can begin to explain the variation in the primary effect of PKU (phenylalanine buildup) and the variation in the pleiotropic effects. Further investigations (especially biochemical studies) of a variety of traits have uncovered many more examples similar to PKU.

[6] This is also a case of epistasis.

The expressivity of a gene may be influenced by the genetic background and/or environmental factors to such a degree that the effects of the gene cannot be seen. In cases where there is overwhelming evidence that someone possesses a gene, yet does not exhibit its effects, it is said that the gene has not penetrated the phenotype or the gene shows incomplete **penetrance**. This is to be distinguished from variable expressivity, where at least some effects of the gene may be seen.

An example of an incompletely penetrant gene in humans is the gene controlling Marfan's syndrome. Affected individuals usually exhibit long limbs and fingers, eye abnormalities, and various heart defects. There is sufficient evidence to suggest that Marfan's syndrome is caused by a dominant gene.

Although the usual characteristics of Marfan's syndrome are stated above, many individuals having the gene causing it show few if any of the manifestations and are only discovered to have the gene when an offspring is recognized as possessing it and a very thorough examination is made of the parent. Often the parent, seemingly not expressing the gene, is found to be rather tall or nearsighted but would never have been diagnosed as having Marfan's syndrome until offspring with the condition were born.

Because some slight manifestation of the syndrome can be found if one looks intensively, Marfan's syndrome may in fact be characterized as a condition with extremely variable expressivity. Another condition, Best's disease, is evidently the result of a dominant gene and is expressed usually as a slight progressive degeneration of the retina with accompanying lesions. Again the expression is extremely variable, ranging from individuals with very slight loss of visual acuity to individuals with rapidly failing vision and hemorrhage of the affected areas (lesions). Since the mode of inheritance is dominant, one would expect only affected parents to have affected offspring. This is generally the case. However, it has been noted that totally unaffected individuals do indeed carry the gene and produce offspring with Best's disease. In these cases the gene does seem to be incompletely penetrant.[7]

Summary

All aspects of the various traits and pathways have not been considered in the last section because of the complex nature of the interactions. However, the discussions will give some idea of how traits are produced and the nature of the final expression of the gene seen in the phenotype. The examples of gene action are not meant to be detailed descriptions but rather introductions

[7]We may return to the concept of a recessive gene and think of it as a gene that does not penetrate the phenotype in the presence of certain other dominant alleles.

62

to the topic. Similarly, the human traits discussed in Chapter 2 are not an exhaustive list, but only those that are fairly simple and reflect the basic laws of heredity. Students wishing to pursue any topics in greater detail will find suggestions for further reading in the following pages.

GLOSSARY

activator—A form of the regulator protein which initiates the synthesis of mRNA of a gene by activating the operator of that gene.

alleles—Alternate forms of genes occurring at the same locus. Each individual has only two alleles at any one locus, but the population may have more than two (for example, ABO blood groups).

assortment—Random distribution of unlinked loci. Mendel's Law of Independent Assortment states that factors controlling separate traits are distributed independently.

autosomes—Chromosomes other than the X and Y chromosomes. Nonsex chromosomes.

base pairs—The adenine-thymine and cytosine-guanine pairs present in DNA.

chromosomes—The dark-staining bodies present in the nucleus. The carriers of genes.

codominance—The approximately equal expression of both alleles in the phenotype.

codon—Three successive bases of a DNA strand specifying an amino acid.

corepressors—End products of a reaction which transform activators to repressors.

DNA—Deoxyribonucleic acid. The genetic material. The molecule that codes for proteins.

dominance—An attribute applied to a trait or its gene which when heterozygous expresses itself over its recessive allele so that the phenotype of the heterozygote is the same as that of the homozygous dominant individual.

epistasis—Interaction between genes at different loci. In epistatic interactions one gene hides or prevents the expression of the other gene.

expressivity—Variations in the manner by which a gene produces a trait.

genotype—The types of genes present at a locus in an individual. More generally it may refer to all genes in an individual.

hemizygous—Referring to the fact that males have only one X chromosome and thus for X-linked genes cannot be homozygous or heterozygous. For X-linked genes males are hemizygous.

heterozygous—Having different alleles at a locus.

homologous chromosomes—The members of a pair of chromosomes which have alleles that control the same traits located at the same locus.

homozygous—Having the same alleles at a locus.

incomplete dominance—The predominance of the action of one gene in the heterozygote. However, both genes are expressed. The least prominent allele is incompletely recessive.

inducers—Initial metabolites, which must be broken down, that transform repressor to activator.

linkage—The presence of separate loci on the same chromosome.

locus—The place on chromosomes which is occupied by alleles.

meiosis—The process by which chromosome number is reduced by half in the formation of gametes. Sex cell division.

mutation—Any alteration in genetic material, such as the change of a codon from ATC to ATG or changes in chromosome structure or number.

nucleotide—A phosphate group, a sugar, and a purine or pyrimidine base linked together.

operator—A gene which controls the production of proteins by other genes through the action of repressors and activators.

operon—Closely linked genes which are regulated through the action of controlling genes (operators and regulators).

penetrance—The ability of a gene to be expressed in the phenotype. Non-penetrance is the absence of expression when the genes for a trait are present.

phenotype—The result of the interaction between genotype and environment. Observed characteristics.

pleiotropism—Manifold effects of one gene. A gene affecting more than one trait.

regulator gene—A gene that produces a protein which controls synthesis of other genes. See **activator**. A form of the regulator protein which stops the synthesis of mRNA of genes by repressing their operator.

RNA—Ribonucleic acid. At least three types of this acid, mRNA, tRNA, and rRNA, are necessary constituents of protein synthesis.

segregation—The independent separation of genes (alleles) controlling the same trait. Mendel's Law of Segregation states that factors controlling a trait are distributed independently.

sex-linked—A term referring to traits controlled by genes on the X or Y chromosome, or, specifically, to X-linked or Y-linked genes.

trait—A structure or characteristic whose expression is controlled by a gene.

transcription—The process of transferring coded information from DNA to mRNA.

translation—The process of transferring coded information from mRNA into the amino acid sequence of a protein.

SUGGESTIONS FOR FURTHER READING

general

Carlson, E. A. 1966. *The gene: A critical history*. Philadelphia: W. B. Saunders.

Levitan, M., and A. Montagu. 1971. *Textbook of human genetics*. New York: Oxford University Press.

Stern, C. 1973. *Principles of human genetics*. 3rd ed. San Francisco: W. H. Freeman and Co.

Strickberger, M. W. 1968. *Genetics*. New York: Macmillan.

chapter one

Fisher, R. A. 1966. *Has Mendel's work been rediscovered?* In *The origin of genetics, a Mendel source book*, C. Stern and E. R. Sherwood (eds.). San Francisco: W. H. Freeman and Co.

Garrod, A. E. 1963. *Inborn errors of metabolism*. New York: Oxford University Press.

Peters, J. A. (ed.). 1959. *Classic papers in genetics*. Englewood Cliffs, New Jersey: Prentice-Hall.

Wright, S. 1966. *Mendel's ratios*. In *The origin of genetics, a Mendel source book*, C. Stern and E. R. Sherwood (eds.). San Francisco: W. H. Freeman and Co.

chapter two

Burdette, W. J. (ed.). 1962. *Methodology in human genetics*. San Francisco: Holden-Day.

McKusick, V. A. 1971. *Mendelian inheritance in man: Catalogs of autosomal recessive and X-linked phenotypes*. 3rd ed. Baltimore: Johns Hopkins Press.

69

McKusick, V. A. 1962. On the X-chromosome of man. *Quarterly Review of Biology* 37:69-175.
Snyder, L. H. 1973. *Blood groups*. Minneapolis: Burgess Publishing Co.

chapter three
Beadle, G. W., and E. L. Tatum. 1941. Genetic control of biochemical reactions in *Neurospora*. *Proceedings of the National Academy of Sciences* 27:499-506.
Crick, F. H. C., L. Barnett, S. Brenner, and R. J. Watts-Tobin. 1961. General nature of the genetic code for proteins. *Nature* 192:1227-32.
Griffith, F. 1923. The significance of pneumococcal types. *Journal of Hygiene* 27:113-59.
Harris, H. 1970. *The principles of biochemical genetics*. Amsterdam: North Holland Publishing Co.
Hershey, A. D., and M. Chase. 1952. Independent functions of viral protein and nucleic acid in growth of bacteriophage. *Journal of General Physiology* 36:39-56.
Jacob, F., and F. Monod. 1961. Genetic regulatory mechanisms in the synthesis of proteins. *Journal of Molecular Biology* 3:318-56.
Levene, P. A., and L. W. Bass. 1931. *Nucleic acids*. New York: Chemical Catalog Co.
Meselson, M., and F. W. Stahl. 1958. The replication of DNA in *Escherichia coli*. *Proceedings of the National Academy of Sciences* 44:671-82.
Nirenberg, M. W., and P. Leder. 1964. RNA codewords and protein synthesis. The effect of trinucleotides upon the binding of sRNA to ribosomes. *Science* 145:1399-1407.
Stanbury, J. B., J. B. Wynogarden, and D. S. Frederickson (eds.). 1972. *The metabolic basis of inherited disease*. 3rd ed. New York: McGraw-Hill.
Taylor, J. H., P. S. Woods, and W. L. Hughes. 1957. The organization and duplication of chromosomes as revealed by autoradiographic studies using tritium-labeled thymidine. *Proceedings of the National Academy of Sciences* 48:122-28.
Watson, J. D. 1970. *The molecular biology of the gene*. 2nd ed. New York: W. A. Benjamin.
Watson, J. D. 1968. *The double helix*. New York: Atheneum Press.

INDEX

DISCARDED